D0463606

DNA—Ladder of Life

DNA-
LADDER
OF
LIFE

by Edward Frankel

illustrated by
Anne Marie Jauss

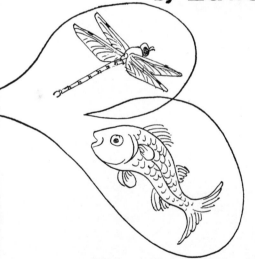

McGRAW-HILL BOOK COMPANY
New York   Toronto   London

To My Wife Helen

Library of Congress Catalog Card Number: 64-24599

FOURTH PRINTING

Introduction

We are now approaching what promises to be one of the greatest scientific triumphs of all times—the control of life. After searching for more than two thousand years, man is at the point of uncovering one of nature's greatest secrets—the molecule which contains the master plan and the chemical control of all living things.

Tremendous in importance as this molecule is, a human cell holds only about a trillionth of an ounce of it. This infinitesimal speck of matter is a molecule named deoxyribonucleic acid, better known by its initials— DNA. The exciting event which is now taking place in many laboratories is the cracking of the code and deciphering of the messages contained in this life-directing molecule.

The discovery of DNA and of RNA, a molecule similar to it, has taken scientists into the submicroscopic world of molecules. New techniques in which biologists manipulate molecules too small to be seen with the most powerful electron microscopes combine the methods of chemistry, physics and mathematics.

Molecular biology made its debut about a decade ago with the unveiling of a three-dimensional model of the DNA molecule by Crick, Watson and Wilkins, the Nobel Prize winners in 1962. Their model, which looks like a twisted ladder, has not only stood the time test of scientific scrutiny but it has also been a reliable guide for those investigating this new science.

DNA research has attracted scientists from many fields the world over because of the promise that molecular biology holds for controlling and perhaps creating life, a feat more daring than the unleashing of atomic energy.

The inspiration and stimulation for writing this book came from the author's students, particularly those of the past decade. The content and ideas for the book were drawn from the thousands of researchers whose findings and thinking appeared in innumerable professional journals, scientific periodicals and books, magazines and newspapers. The names of only a few of these contributors appear in the text.

The author wishes to express thanks to his colleagues, friends and students who made helpful suggestions, many of which are incorporated in this book. Special mention is made of Helen Frankel, wife of the author, for her invaluable assistance in reading and correcting the manuscript during the various phases of its development. Finally, special appreciation is expressed to a former student, Dr. Norton D. Zinder, Professor at the Rockefeller Institute, for his critical reading of the complete manuscript. For any inaccuracies which may appear, the author is solely responsible.

Contents

1

DNA—The Molecule of Life

One of the most thrilling scientific advances of modern times is the discovery of a molecule that determines the basic nature of all life, from the simplest microbe to man himself. This molecule is present in every one of the billions of cells in your body. It is best known by the letters DNA, which are the initials for its chemical name—deoxyribonucleic (pronounced day-OX-ee-rye-bow-new-CLAY-ic) acid. The nucleic acid part of the name tells you that DNA is an acid located in the nucleus of the living cell.

DNA was first isolated from the nuclei of white blood cells and fish sperm cells about 100 years ago. Its importance to life, however, did not become known until a decade or so ago. Although the details of DNA structure are far too small to be seen with even the most powerful microscope, scientists have worked out its structure and chemical composition. They are discovering how DNA directs the processes of life in each organism. Today we are on the threshold of unlocking life's greatest secret— the genetic code—which will reveal how DNA dictates the transmission of characteristics from parent to off- spring. Once this mystery has been solved, it may be pos- sible to create life in a test tube.

DNA, then, exercises dual control over the life of an organism. It directs metabolism, the day to day activities that keep the machinery of the body turning. It also de- termines heredity, the transmission of traits that keeps the race or species going for hundreds, thousands, and some- times millions of years.

Living requires an endless flow of molecules in and out of an organism. Some of the incoming molecules are burned to provide the energy needed to power the living thing. Other molecules are transformed into the material of which the organism is composed and are used for repair, replacement, and growth. Life is an endless chain of met- abolic activities and molecule manipulations which are directed and controlled by DNA.

A remarkable capacity of a living thing is its ability to reproduce, to create another very much like itself. The striking resemblance between parents and their offspring suggests that some substance is passed on from one genera- tion to the next which determines specific traits. One of the great scientific breakthroughs in recent years was the disclosure that the DNA molecule is that material. Within a living cell, this molecule is able to make an exact duplicate of itself and send the copy on to direct the next generation.

The Case of the Deadly Microbes

Early clues about the nature of DNA came from the study of the strange behavior of certain disease-causing microbes, the pneumonia germs. There are, in general, two kinds of pneumonia bacteria, one with a jelly-like coat and the other without this coat. Research showed that only the coated microbes caused pneumonia.

Back in 1928, Fred Griffith, an English bacteriologist, was experimenting with these pneumonia organisms. Using heat, he killed some of the coated germs and then injected mice with a mixture of these killed coated ones and live, harmless, uncoated microbes. From what was then known about these microbes, the mice should have remained alive and healthy. Instead, the animals developed pneumonia and died. Moreover, while the bodies of these dead mice swarmed with coated pneumonia germs, the harmless, uncoated ones could not be found. Griffith thought perhaps the killed coated germs which he injected were not really dead. He therefore injected other mice with only some dead germs from the original batch. Not one of these animals became sick. Apparently the dead germs were really dead. In some mysterious way, the uncoated microbes acquired a coat and became deadly. Evidently the dead germs passed something on to the living microbes that changed them and their offspring. What was that something?

Scientists spent the next few years puzzling over how

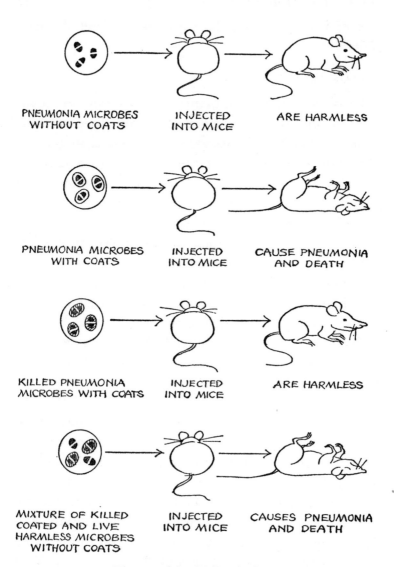

PNEUMONIA MICROBES
WITHOUT COATS

INJECTED
INTO MICE

ARE HARMLESS

PNEUMONIA MICROBES
WITH COATS

INJECTED
INTO MICE

CAUSE PNEUMONIA
AND DEATH

KILLED PNEUMONIA
MICROBES WITH COATS

INJECTED
INTO MICE

ARE HARMLESS

MIXTURE OF KILLED
COATED AND LIVE
HARMLESS MICROBES
WITHOUT COATS

INJECTED
INTO MICE

CAUSES PNEUMONIA
AND DEATH

The case of the deadly microbes

harmless uncoated microbes changed into deadly coated ones. This mystery was finally cleared up in 1944 by Dr. Oswald T. Avery and two of his colleagues at the Rockefeller Institute in New York City. They not only isolated but also identified the substance responsible for transforming these microbes. Avery extracted from the dead coated pneumonia germs, a substance which could be collected as long fine threads. When harmless pneumonia microbes were grown in a solution of these threads, some of them acquired a coat and became deadly. Equally astonishing, the change was permanent. All the offspring of the transformed microbes had coats and caused pneumonia.

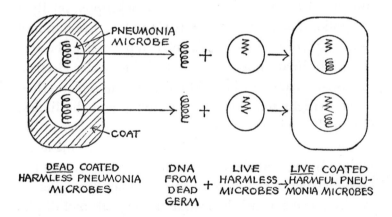

DEAD COATED HARMLESS PNEUMONIA MICROBES + DNA FROM DEAD GERM + LIVE HARMLESS MICROBES → LIVE COATED HARMFUL PNEUMONIA MICROBES

Avery and his team discovered that this dramatic inherited change was due to a single chemical substance found in the long fine threads, DNA. DNA had carried the disease-causing trait from the harmful to the harmless bacteria. This experiment clearly established DNA as the specific carrier of hereditary information. Scientists were able to draw this conclusion because they observed that the DNA of one kind of organism got into another kind of organism and changed it permanently. Thus the case of the strange behavior of the dead pneumonia that seemed to come to life was solved by scientific sleuthing. The mysterious and magical transformer was DNA.

Viruses—Packaged DNA

Another fertile source of information about DNA has come from the study of the simplest and smallest bits of living material, the viruses. They are the cause of such human diseases as measles, mumps, chickenpox, smallpox and polio. The average virus is about one five-hundred-thousandth of an inch long, much too small to be seen with an ordinary microscope but visible under electron-microscope magnifications. The size of viruses places them in the twilight zone between the living and the lifeless. The smallest viruses are about the size of the largest life-less molecules. The largest viruses are about as big as the smallest living microbes. Viruses can behave either as life-less molecules or as living organisms. They can appear as a white powder which looks like salt crystals and display no more life than this lifeless chemical. On the other hand, once a tiny virus crystal gains entry into a cell, it can come to "life" and breed new viruses at the fantastic rate of ten per minute. The virus is a parasite. It can grow and reproduce only inside a living cell. The virus may be

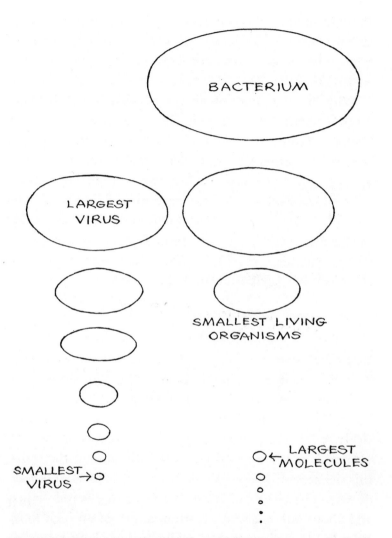

The size of viruses places them in the twilight zone between the living and the lifeless, that is, between the largest molecules and the smallest living organisms

thought of as an incomplete cell. It comes to life only inside a complete cell that supplies it with the missing parts. Some viruses eat, live, and reproduce inside bacteria, which are tiny cells.

Why has the study of viruses yielded so much information about DNA? Chemically, viruses are extremely simple when compared to other living things, composed as they are only of those molecules absolutely necessary for life. They are made of just two substances, proteins and nucleic acid, welded together to make a giant molecule of nucleoproteins. The nucleic acid is coiled inside the protein coat which covers and protects it. In most viruses, the nucleic acid is DNA, a few contain a related chemical, RNA, ribonucleic acid.

Protein Coats and Nucleic Acid Cores

In 1955 Dr. Heinz Fraenkel-Conrat, a biochemist in the Virus Laboratory at the University of California, conducted a crucial experiment that shed light on DNA as the basic molecule of life. He was studying the tobacco mosaic virus, TMV, which infects the tobacco plant and causes sickly yellow spots to appear on the leaves where the viruses have eaten away the tissues. Because of the spots, this sickness of tobacco plants is known as tobacco mosaic disease. The virus which causes this disease is rod-shaped and about one one-hundred-thousandth of an inch long. It looks like a piece of thick-walled tubing housing a core of cable wire. The cylindrical wall, which is made of protein, surrounds a delicate coiled fiber of nucleic acid.

Fraenkel-Conrat performed a most delicate and difficult feat in biochemical surgery. He separated the protein coats from the nucleic acid cores. Using a detergent, he dissolved the protein coats from one batch of TMV, leaving a mass of nucleic acid fibers. He then treated another group of TMV particles with a different chemical that ate away the inner nucleic acid core, leaving empty protein containers.

He was now ready for the crucial experiment. Which part of the virus was alive—which part could cause the tobacco disease—the protein coat or the nucleic acid core? A drop of a solution containing the protein coats was rubbed on the leaf of a healthy tobacco plant, and some

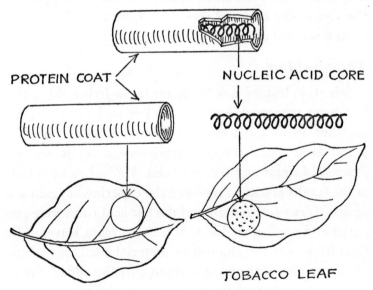

PROTEIN COAT

NUCLEIC ACID CORE

TOBACCO LEAF

Nucleic acid cores alone cause tobacco mosaic disease

of the nucleic acid cores on another leaf. After a few days, Fraenkel-Conrat examined the leaves and found all of them spotless. Neither the coats nor the cores, when separated, showed any signs of life. The coats were then mixed with the threads and applied to the leaf. This time yellow spots showed up, identical with those produced by the natural living virus. This meant that the virus was alive— it caused the tobacco mosaic disease. An examination of some of this mixture under the electron microscope revealed coats containing cores. The nucleic acid threads prepared from one batch of viruses had slipped into the empty protein coats of another and were completely at home. These viruses not only looked but behaved as if they had never been taken apart. Evidently both parts of the virus—the coat and the core—were essential for life, or so it seemed at first.

Threads of Life

Scientific history was being made—a living thing that had been separated into two lifeless molecules was put together again and was alive. Life had been created in a test tube from lifeless chemicals—or so it seemed. Fraenkel-Conrat was very cautious. He had to be certain of the results and so he repeated the experiment again and again. More protein coats and nucleic acid cores were prepared and applied to different tobacco plant leaves. This time he varied the amount of material used. No matter what quantity of the coats without cores he added, the tobacco leaves showed no yellow spots; the proteins were lifeless. However, when the amount of nucleic acid cores normally present in the virus was increased a thousand fold and then rubbed into a leaf, the plant developed the tobacco disease. Why did this happen?

Nucleic acid fibers are extremely fragile and are easily broken in the process of preparing them. This is what happened in the earlier experiment. To be infectious, the entire unbroken thread must enter the plant cell. Broken nucleic acid fibers lose the power to cause the disease. When enough of these fibers are extracted, a few escape injury, remain intact, and are infectious. The coiled core of the virus alone, the nucleic acid molecule, is the thread of life.

Thus the study of the virus has led to the basic molecule of life DNA. In the case of the tobacco mosaic virus, the nucleic acid is actually RNA, ribonucleic acid, but it does for this virus what DNA does for most other living things —gives them life. The lowest common denominators of life are the nucleic acids—RNA for a few viruses and DNA for practically all the other organisms.

DNA is the "spark of life," the master molecule that designs all the other molecules of life.

2

The Cell—The House of DNA

There are more than a million kinds of plants and animals, and they display tremendous differences in size, shape, and way of living. Nevertheless all organisms—from amoebas to zinnias—are composed of very similar units, cells. These are the building blocks and the centers of life.

A most remarkable property of a living cell is its ability to maintain its structure and chemical composition in spite of the constant coming and going of billions of molecules every moment. The tremendous task of preserving the structure and function of a living cell is largely the work of DNA.

With few exceptions, cells are so small they can be seen only through a microscope. Some organisms such as bacteria and amoebas are microscopic in size and consist of one cell. This one-celled organism eats, breathes, digests, excretes, moves, and reproduces. Most organisms consist of a great many cells and the work of living is divided among them. Some cells in your body enable you to move, others carry messages, and still others distribute oxygen. Groups of cooperating cells form tissues, and tissues make up the organs of your body—the heart, liver, kidneys, brain. All of these are members of an organization of ten trillion cells engaged in keeping you alive.

Cell Parts

Cells are remarkably uniform in basic design. As seen through an ordinary microscope, most of them have a single central body, the nucleus (NEW-klee-us) embedded in a jelly-like layer called the cytoplasm (SIGH-toe-plazm). There is a very thin membrane around the cytoplasm, the cell membrane, and another around the nucleus, the nuclear membrane.

Cytoplasm—The Sea of Molecules

The cytoplasm is a colorless liquid containing mostly water in which there are myriads of molecules—carbohydrates, fats, proteins, minerals, vitamins, and many others. This sea of assorted molecules that bathes the nucleus is the source of all the materials required by DNA to conduct its business. The cytoplasm contains many tiny structures, each with a particular job. For example, there are from 50 to 50,000 bean-shaped structures scattered throughout the cytoplasm that generate the energy needed for doing the work of the cell. These "power plants," called mitochondria (my-toe-KON-dree-uh), are capable of extracting energy from the food molecules floating around in the cytoplasm.

Nucleus—Director

The control center of the cell is the nucleus. This single spherical or egg-shaped structure contains at least one large granule called a nucleolus (new-KLEE-oh-lis) or little nucleus, and many finer granules referred to as chromatin (CROW-muh-tin), which means color. These granules stain very readily with certain dyes making them stand out very clearly under the microscope. When the cell is ready to reproduce, the chromatin granules collect into pairs of thread-like structures known as chromosomes (CROW-muh-zomes) or colored bodies.

Chromosomes

The cells of each kind of organism contain a specific and characteristic number of chromosomes referred to as the species number. For man, the species number is 46 (or 23 pairs of) chromosomes; in the house fly, it is 12 (or 6 pairs); and in the corn plant, 20 (or 10 pairs).

The chromosomes contain the hereditary material of an organism, that is, the material passed on from parent to offspring and responsible for the great resemblance between them. Beginning at the turn of the century, the chromosome was pictured as containing thousands of hereditary units, the genes, strung together like beads on a

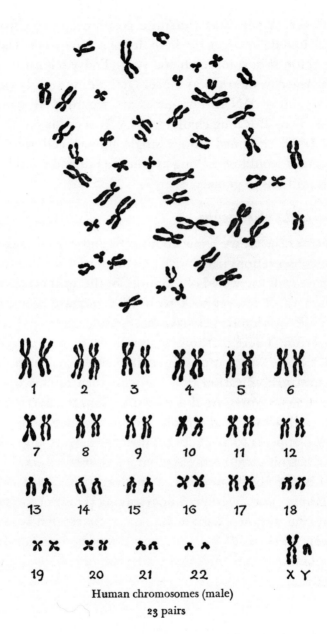

Human chromosomes (male)

23 pairs

necklace. A gene has a definite position on the chromo-some and determines the heredity of some specific trait—eye color, skin color, or blood type. Today scientists visu-alize the chromosome as a package holding tightly coiled molecules of DNA. The genes are regarded as spots or areas along this long chain of DNA. It is estimated that if the DNA crammed into a single human cell were un-wound it would be as long as you are tall and would con-tain millions of genes.

The Light Microscope

Most of what we know about cells and microbes comes from observations made with a light microscope. Since the discovery of the world of microbes in the 17th century by Anton van Leeuwenhoek with his 200-power single-lens magnifier, microscopes have been made more and more powerful. There is, however, a limit to the power of microscopes which use ordinary light and glass lenses. The greatest magnification possible with such microscopes is about 2,000 times. At this magnification, the average hu-man cell, which is about one two-thousandth of an inch across, appears to be about an inch long. More important than magnification is the resolving power of a microscope, that is, the ability to distinguish clearly between two ob-jects very close together. The resolving power of the mod-ern light microscope is about 100,000 times; that is, it can clearly distinguish between two lines one one-hundred-thousandth of an inch apart. It enables you to see tiny bacteria but not viruses or the giant molecules of life such as DNA or RNA.

The Electron Microscope

The electron microscope at present can magnify a few hundred thousand times and resolve objects about one ten-millionth of an inch apart. By using a beam of electrons, which have a much shorter wave length than that of light, greater magnifications and resolutions can be achieved. The bending and focusing of the electron beam is done by electromagnets instead of glass lenses. Electrons are emitted by a heated tungsten filament similar to that in a light bulb. The electrons stream through a vacuum tube about 4 feet long and pass through the object in the same way that X rays penetrate flesh and bones. The enlarged image may be focused either on a photographic plate or directly on a viewing screen similar to that in a television set. Improvement in the electron microscope continues to be made. Dr. Alvar P. Wilska of the University of Arizona is working on a new design which promises magnifications and resolutions with which it should be possible to see atoms. He believes that with this new electron microscope, the fine atomic structure of DNA, RNA, and proteins will be seen directly.

The Cell Through the Electron Microscope

When a cell is viewed through an electron microscope, many new and unexpected cellular details are revealed.

The electron microscope

The cytoplasm which, under the light microscope, seems to be a shapeless, formless liquid, at electron microscope magnification appears to be riddled with a network of interconnecting canals called the endoplasmic reticulum (en-doe-PLAZ-mick re-TICK-you-lum). This system of canals seems to start at the outer cell membrane, meanders through the cytoplasm and eventually connects with the membrane surrounding the nucleus. It may be the roadway for the transportation of molecules from the outside throughout the cell down to the nucleus. The walls of these canals are covered with thousands of very fine particles called ribosomes (RYE-bo-zomes), so named because they are rich in RNA, ribonucleic acid. Ribosomes are the protein-producing centers of the cell. At electron microscope magnifications, mitochondrions, which are the power plants of the cell, have a covering consisting of two layers. The outer one is smooth but the inner membrane is folded inward to form compartments. The surfaces of both membranes are sprinkled with thousands of tiny particles that carry out the energy-releasing chemical reactions. Another interesting detail revealed by the electron microscope is the structure of the nuclear membrane. It also appears to be a double membrane with fine perforations in the layer facing the cytoplasm.

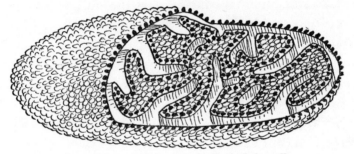

The mitochondrion—power plant of the cell

Incomplete Cells

The virus is, in a sense, an incomplete cell and therefore an incomplete organism. It lacks a cell membrane and cytoplasm. In chemical composition and in behavior, viruses and chromosomes are very much alike. Both are giant molecules of nucleoproteins and both reproduce themselves only inside cells. The chromosome uses the cytoplasm of the cell in which it is housed as a source of molecules; the virus lives on the borrowed cytoplasm of its host cell. The virus has been aptly described as a hungry piece of chromosome looking for a cell.

Cells in Technicolor

Many structures in a living cell are either invisible or very difficult to see even when they are greatly magnified. With the addition of certain dyes, hidden cellular structures become visible and distinct parts come into sharp focus under the microscope. One such dye is methylene blue, which stains nuclear parts dark blue, particularly the chromosomes, and makes them stand out very clearly. A combination of methylene blue and another dye, eosin (EE-oh-sin), simultaneously colors the nucleus blue and the cytoplasm pink. Dyes are also useful in identifying the chemical composition of cell parts. Acid fuchsin (FEWK-sin) is a dye which colors DNA reddish-purple. When it is applied to a cell, only the chromosomes stain that color, indicating that DNA is located only in the nucleus. Another dye, azure B, colors DNA blue-green and RNA purple. With this dye, the chomosomes stain blue-green and the nucleolus and cytoplasm appear purple. These staining reactions place DNA in the chromosomes and RNA in the nucleolus and cytoplasm.

The Cell as a Chemical Factory

The cell is indeed a very complex and busy chemical factory carrying on the big business of living. It is a marvel in miniature construction, with many built-in parts each playing its role in the countless activities going on

in the cells. We will see in the chapters that follow how
the DNA in the nucleus acts as the master planner and
master builder, and RNA as the contractor. The ribo-

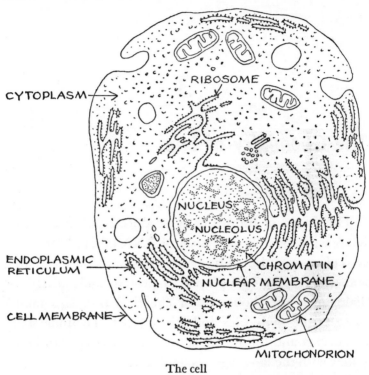

The cell

somes are the protein-producing machines, the mitochondria the power stations, the endoplasmic reticulum the
channels for transportation of materials, and the cytoplasm the source of myriads of molecules, while the cell
membrane is the gateway which controls the movement
of molecules in and out of the premises. The basic
chemical substances and the chemical reactions of life are
our next concern.

3

The Chemistry of Life

The drama of life which is produced and directed by
DNA with the able assistance of RNA takes place in the
cells of an organism. The actors are atoms and molecules,
with the leading role played by protein molecules. The
dialogue is the thousands of chemical processes taking
place as the molecules and atoms react. To understand
this drama and follow the action, it is necessary to be familiar with the language of chemistry.

Elements and Atoms

The letters in the alphabet of basic chemistry are the
elements, the basic materials of which everything in the
universe is made. An atom is the smallest part of an
element and it cannot be broken down into anything
simpler and still remain the same substance. There are
103 elements known today, ninety-two of which are found

naturally. The remainder have been produced in the past
twenty years. Some elements you know by name—oxygen,
hydrogen, carbon, nitrogen, iron, mercury, and uranium.
Others, with names ranging from actinium to zirconium,
may be unfamiliar to you. About a dozen elements are
very common, and compose most of the things around you.

The smallest particle of an element, iron for example,
is an atom of iron. Since there are 103 elements, there are
103 different kinds of atoms. An atom is very small. A
quarter of a billion hydrogen atoms, when lined up side
by side, would occupy only one inch.

Compounds and Molecules

Atoms tend to join with one another, forming groups
referred to as molecules. The atoms in a molecule may be
the same or they may be different. A molecule of water,
for example, contains three atoms, two of hydrogen and
one of oxygen. The atoms in a molecule of an element are
always the same. Oxygen, the gas found in air, consists of
molecules each of which contains two atoms of oxygen.
Molecules in which the atoms are different are called compounds. Water is a compound since a molecule of it contains two different kinds of atoms, namely, hydrogen and
oxygen.

If you think of the 103 elements as the letters in the
chemical alphabet, and compounds as the words formed
by these letters, it becomes clear that the number of possible chemical words or compounds exceeds that in all
spoken and written languages in the world.

Chemical Symbols

The chemist uses a shorthand system for writing the names of the elements and compounds. In this system, the first letter of the name of the element is frequently used as a chemical symbol. For example, O represents oxygen, N stands for nitrogen, C is the symbol for carbon, and so on. Since there are only twenty-six letters in the alphabet and a different symbol is assigned to each element, some are represented by two letters, such as Al for aluminum, Ca for calcium, and Cl for chlorine. The symbols for molecules are derived from the symbols of the atoms they contain just as words are the combinations of letters. A molecule of oxygen with its two atoms is written as O_2, the compound water as H_2O, and carbon dioxide as CO_2. Two molecules of water are $2H_2O$ and four of carbon dioxide, $4CO_2$.

The Elements of Life

Living things are made principally of six kinds of atoms. Your body, for example, is 65% oxygen (O), 18% carbon (C), 10% hydrogen (H), 3% nitrogen (N), 2% sulfur (S), and 1% phosphorus (P). These six elements account for 97% of your weight. About twenty-five additional elements make up the rest of you. They include calcium, potassium, sodium, chlorine, magnesium, iron, iodine, fluorine, copper, zinc, and cobalt.

The six elements of life—C, O, H, N, S, and P—are neither rare nor restricted to living things. Air is almost entirely O_2 and N_2; water is H_2O, and the other elements are in the earth—C in coal and S and P in rocks and soil.

A distinctive feature of living material is the kinds of molecules they form from these elements. The molecules associated with life are usually large, complicated, and fragile. They contain hundreds, thousands, and sometimes millions of atoms. One of the largest known molecules, the

	AIR	LAND	SEA	LIFE
1.	OXYGEN	OXYGEN	OXYGEN	OXYGEN
2.	NITROGEN			NITROGEN
3.		SILICON		
4.		ALUMINUM		
5.		IRON		
6.		CALCIUM		
7.			HYDROGEN	HYDROGEN
8.			CHLORINE	
9.			SODIUM	
10				CARBON
11.				SULFUR
12.				PHOSPHORUS

tobacco mosaic virus, is a giant molecule of nucleoprotein containing over 5 million atoms. There are, however, only six kinds of atoms in this monster molecule—C, O, H, N, S, and P. The molecules of the nucleic acids, DNA and RNA, may contain hundreds of thousands of atoms but they are limited to only five kinds—C, O, H, N, and P.

Atomic Structure

The kinds of atoms that combine and the way in which they join are governed by chemical rules and regulations. To understand these chemical reactions, you must know something about the structure of atoms.

All atoms, with the exception of hydrogen atoms, consist of three basic particles—electrons, protons, and neutrons. Electrons are negatively charged particles that whirl around a dense central core or nucleus containing the protons and neutrons. Protons are positively charged particles. Neutrons have no charge.

Each kind of atom has a different number of basic particles. Hydrogen, for example, consists of just one electron and one proton; carbon contains six electrons, six protons, and six neutrons; nitrogen has seven of each, and oxygen eight. Since the number of electrons in an atom is equal to the number of protons, the atom is electrically neutral.

Electrons in Orbit

The electrons revolve around the nucleus of an atom along definite paths or orbits located at varying distances from the nucleus. Each orbit can hold only a certain number of electrons. The first orbit, which is nearest the nucleus, has no more than two electrons, the second orbit, which is further out, is limited to eight, and the third holds as many as eighteen.

The single electron of H occupies the first orbit. The six electrons of carbon are distributed so that two are in the first orbit and the other four in the second. Hydrogen lacks one to complete its outermost ring. Carbon lacks four and oxygen, with six electrons in its outermost orbit, needs two. The behavior of a particular kind of atom in relation to other atoms is influenced by the number of electrons in its orbital rings. Atoms tend to fill up their outermost orbits by either taking electrons from other atoms, or giving up all the electrons in their outer ring to another atom, or by sharing their electrons with another

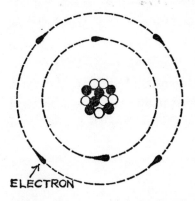

ELECTRON

A carbon atom contains six electrons, six protons, and six neutrons

atom. In general, elements with less than four orbital electrons tend to lose them to other atoms, those with more than four tend to take electrons from other atoms, and those with four tend to compromise, being neither lenders nor borrowers but sharers of electrons. Atoms capable of exchanging or sharing electrons can undergo chemical reactions and form new molecules. The energy holding the atoms together in the molecule is called a *chemical bond*. Each atom has a definite and limited number of chemical bonds, which may be thought of as links connecting it with other atoms.

Chemical Bonds

Since we are primarily interested in living organisms and the chemical reaction of life, let us examine the chemical bonds of the six elements of life. The hydrogen atom has only one chemical bond and it can be represented as H—. Since carbon has four outer orbital electrons and room for four more, it has four chemical bonds and is therefore symbolized as —C̷—. Oxygen, with six electrons in its outermost ring, has room for two more and it therefore is represented with two bonds as —O—. Nitrogen, with five electrons, has three chemical bonds and is represented as —N̷—. Similarly, sulfur with two chemical bonds is —S— and phosphorus with three is represented by —P̷—.

Molecules—Bonded Atoms

It is now possible to understand how some very simple molecules are formed. For example, H— can combine with another H— to form H_2 which may also be written as H—H. H_2 is the molecular formula which tells you that a molecule of hydrogen contains two atoms of hydrogen. H—H is the structural formula which gives you some idea of the arrangement of the atoms in the molecule. Four H—'s can also join with —C̷— to form CH_4, which is

A water molecule, H_2O, contains one atom of oxygen linked to two atoms of hydrogen

known as methane, a gas found in swamps and in natural gas used as fuel. —Ṅ— can hook onto three H—'s to form NH₃, ammonia, a gas that is present in a household cleaner.

Atoms may be linked not only by single bonds but also by double or triple bonds. A molecule of oxygen is O═O, Nitrogen is N≡N.

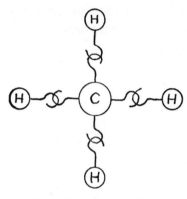

Methane
CH_4 — four hydrogen atoms joined to one carbon atom

Carbon Compounds

The large complex molecules so characteristic of living matter—such as carbohydrates, fats, proteins, and nucleic acids—are carbon compounds. They are built around a backbone of carbon atoms arranged in a chain. Although carbon has four chemical bonds, which can join with four other atoms, it exhibits the properties of self-linkage, more so than any other atom. Carbon atoms have the tendency to join one another, forming long stable chains or rings.

Carbon Chains

Starting with a simple one-carbon compound, methane

(CH₄), you can build a two-carbon chain by joining another methane molecule to it. By linking a third methane to the two-carbon chain, you can extend it to a three-carbon linkage. This process can be extended on and on and the chain may grow in a straight line or it can become branched.

The sugar found commonly in fruits has a six-carbon chain, $C_6H_{12}O_6$. The sugars present in the nucleic acids ribose and deoxyribose are both five-carbon sugars, $C_5H_{10}O_5$ and $C_5H_{10}O_4$ respectively.

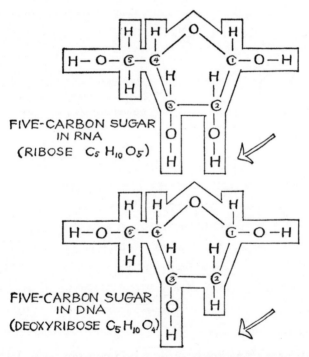

Sugars present in the nucleic acids

Rings of Carbon

The carbon atoms at one end of the chain may join with those at the other to make a closed ring. The ring may contain six carbon atoms connected by alternating single and double bonds. One of the simplest of these ring compounds has a hydrogen atom attached to each of the six carbon atoms; it is C_6H_6, benzene.

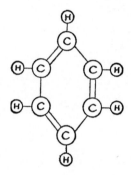

Benzene—C_6H_6

The ring may contain nitrogen or some other elements in addition to carbon. There may be four carbon and two nitrogen atoms in the ring. This is the basic structure of the pyrimidines (Pih-RIM-ih-deans) such as thymine (THIGH-mean) and cytosine (SIGH-toe-seen) (both parts of the DNA molecule) and uracil (YOUR-a-sill), found in RNA.

Another arrangement is a combination of rings such as is found in the purines (PURE-eens). Adenine (ADD-

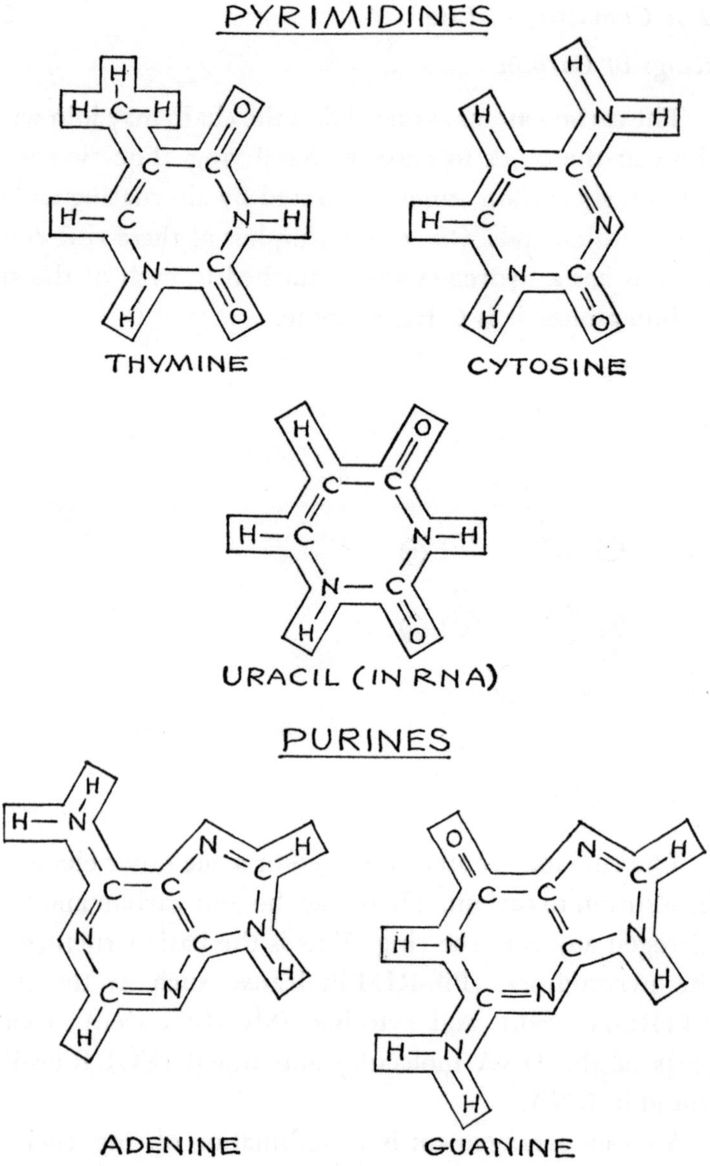

PYRIMIDINES

THYMINE

CYTOSINE

URACIL (IN RNA)

PURINES

ADENINE

GUANINE

Bases in DNA and RNA

uh-neen) and guanine (GUAH-neen) are such double-ringed molecules found in DNA and RNA.

Now that you have been introduced to some of the basic chemical reactions of life and some of the molecules involved, you can begin to understand the importance of molecular architecture, particularly of DNA, the basic molecule of life. This is our next consideration.

4

DNA—The Ladder of Life

The Nobel Prize in Medicine and Physiology for 1962 was awarded to an American and two British scientists for their "discovery of the molecular structure of deoxyribonucleic acid, DNA, which contributed to an understanding of the basic life processes." The winners were Dr. James D. Watson of Harvard University in Cambridge, Massachusetts, Dr. Francis H. C. Crick of Cambridge University in England, and Dr. Maurice H. F. Wilkins of Kings College in London.

Their discoveries have been hailed as perhaps the most significant advance in biology in the present century. To the world of science, these men were no strangers, and this recognition came as no great surprise. The Crick-Watson model of DNA, which looks like a twisted ladder, has been a familiar symbol since 1953 when it was first suggested by this team. Their model is helping to solve the mystery of the architecture of this all-powerful, all-purpose molecule and to explain how DNA governs life. It provides us with a physical explanation of how DNA carries hereditary information and also how this information is passed on from cell to cell and from organism to organism.

The Mighty Midget

All the DNA in a human egg cell weighs about a ten-trillionth of an ounce and measures in the hundred-millionths of an inch. Nevertheless, the DNA in this single cell holds all the hereditary information necessary to guide its development into a full grown man or woman. Although DNA is unbelievably small, it contains an incredible amount of genetic information, enough to fill a thousand-volume encyclopedia.

X-Ray Pictures of DNA

By 1950 DNA was recognized as the master molecule containing genetic instructions that determined the form and function of each living thing. Scientists became intrigued with the atomic architecture of this molecule, that is, how the atoms and groups of atoms are arranged in DNA. They felt that knowledge of its composition and an understanding of how it is put together would provide the key for explaining how it works.

Electron-microscope studies revealed little about its architecture since DNA is incredibly thin, about one one-millionth of an inch thick, and at electron-microscope magnifications, it looked like a stiff piece of string without internal structure.

The shape and construction of this molecule, too small to be seen with the most powerful microscope, was explored by another method which involved studying its shadow. You can place a light source behind an object and cast its shadow on a wall or screen. Suppose you are on the other side of the screen and cannot see the object, your brother, for example. You could probably identify him by moving him around and obtaining shadows, from different angles.

This is essentially what Dr. Wilkins did; however, he used X ray instead of light to study samples of pure DNA obtained from various organisms. By bouncing X rays off the atoms in the DNA molecule, Wilkins obtained photographs of their atomic architecture. These are not pictures in the ordinary sense of the word but shadow or silhouette patterns. When X rays strike an atom or group of atoms they are scattered or deflected from their paths and cast shadows on a photographic plate. Groups of regularly repeating or orderly arranged atoms can be identified by the shadow pictures they produce. The X-ray pictures suggested that the DNA molecule is twisted into a spring or coil resembling a spiral staircase or twisted ladder. The steps are flat units stacked one above the other perpendicular to the length of the thread-like molecule, like the steps in a circular staircase. The shape of the DNA molecules of all organisms is the same, regardless of whether they come from a bacterium, fish, or human.

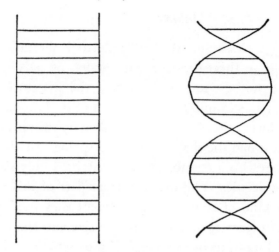

DNA has the shape of a twisted ladder

Six Pieces

Chemical studies revealed that DNA is one of the largest molecules known, composed of many thousands of atoms. However, these huge molecules are constructed from smaller submolecular units, which are used over and over again as building blocks. DNA contains six kinds of submolecular building blocks. One of them is the sugar deoxyribose, the D in DNA. Another is phosphate, a group of four oxygen and one phosphorus atoms. The other four units are purine and pyrimidine, rings of carbon and nitrogen atoms referred to in the previous chapter. They are adenine, guanine, thymine, and cytosine, collectively known as bases. We shall refer to them by the first letters of their names—A, G, T, and C. Sugars, phosphates, and bases—these are the structural parts. But how are they assembled in the DNA molecule?

Molecular Model Makers

In 1952 Crick and Watson undertook the task of constructing a three-dimensional model of DNA. They thought the best way to determine the structure of this molecule was to build a scale model of it. The only clues they had were the X-ray pictures taken by Wilkins suggesting that it had the shape of a coiled spring or twisted ladder. They also knew that DNA contained only six kinds of submolecules. The most unusual part of this venture was the kind of laboratory equipment they used. It consisted of pieces of metal cut in the size and shape of the six building units of DNA and wire to act as the chemical bonds for joining the pieces.

For a year these model makers struggled with this chemical jig-saw puzzle, using imagination and ingenuity to get the pieces to fit together according to all that was known about the chemical and physical structure of DNA. Finally, the pieces fell into place and they came up with their 3-D scale model.

Crick-Watson Model

How do the six building units fit into the model? The model that Crick and Watson assembled in 1953 resembles a twisted ladder. The sides of this ladder, which are two long threads wound around each other, contain alternating sugar and phosphate units. The rungs, which are flat units stacked one above the other, are attached at right angles to the sugar units in the two twisted threads. Each

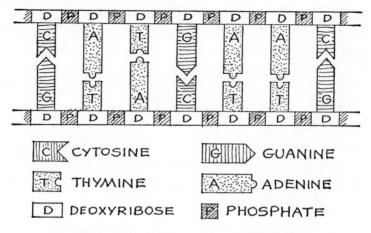

```
|C|K CYTOSINE          |G|||||> GUANINE
|T|Ç THYMINE           |A| :> ADENINE
|D| DEOXYRIBOSE        |P| PHOSPHATE
```

How the six building units fit into the DNA molecule

rung consists of a pair of bases, either an A and a T, or a C and a G. No other combination of bases is found in the rungs of the DNA ladder. The A-T and C-G pairs of bases make rungs of equal length and of the proper size to fit between the parallel sides of the ladder; other combinations are either too large or too small. Also, only A can join with a T, and G with C, because these bases have matching shapes, like pieces in a jig-saw puzzle. The matched pairs of bases are fastened together by hydrogen bonds, A and T by two, and C and G by three.

Thus an A in strand 1, the left side of the ladder, is hydrogen bonded to T in strand 2, the right side of the ladder. T in strand 1 is paired with A in strand 2. G in strand 1 is wedded to C in strand 2, and C in strand 1 is connected to G in strand 2. A is bonded to T, and G to C. Hence the order of the bases in one strand fixes the order of the bases in strand 2. For example, when the bases in strand 1 are CATGAAC, the order of the bases in strand 2 is GTACTTG.

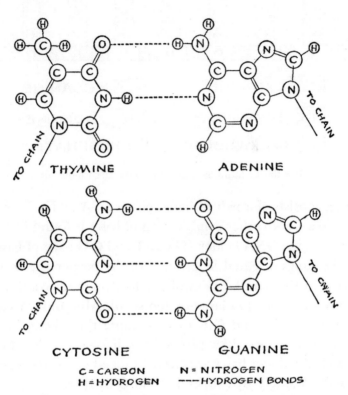

Matched pairs of DNA bases are linked by hydrogen bonds

The ground rules governing the structure of the Crick-Watson model of DNA may be summarized as follows:

1. DNA consists of two intertwining strands which resemble a twisted ladder.

2. Each of the strands consists of a chain of alternating sugar and phosphate units.

3. The individual rungs of the ladder, stacked one above the other and at right angles to the twisted threads, contain pairs of bases.

4. There are only four kinds of rungs: A-T, T-A, C-G, and G-C.

5. The sequence of bases in one strand determines and fixes the sequence of bases in the second strand.

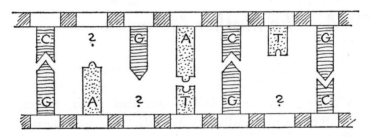

What units are missing?

Now that you are familiar with the Crick-Watson Model of DNA, let us see how it can be used to explain some of the fundamental problems of life such as how DNA carries genetic information and how this information is duplicated.

5

DNA—The Mother Molecule

A unique feature of DNA—one that distinguishes it from all other molecules—is its ability to duplicate itself. This "mother" molecule can make another molecule exactly like itself and the duplicate may be passed on to its descendants. These molecules are links in the chain of life that stretch back in time for as long as the species has existed. Each new cell or organism begins its life with a set of hereditary instructions built into the structure of its DNA molecule which "tells" it what kind of an organism it is and what to do.

Self-duplication is a fundamental property of life. A bacterium reproduces every twenty minutes by simply splitting in half. Every time it reproduces, its DNA duplicates and the copy containing the blueprints for making another bacterium like itself goes to the new organism.

Similarly, each new generation of human beings receives the genetic instructions for human beings from the previous generation.

DNA Duplication in the Virus

The self-duplicating powers of the DNA molecule can be seen in viruses that feed on bacteria. Such viruses are called bacteriophages (bak-TEAR-ee-o-fay-jez) or phages for short. Viruses, you may remember, are the smallest and simplest bits of life capable of growing and reproducing, but only inside the cell of another organism. These parasites are giant molecules of nucleoprotein, with a protein coat and a nucleic acid core. The phage or virus called T2 lives on bacteria which commonly inhabit the human intestines. T2 is tadpole-shaped with a six-sided hollow head and a long hollow tail at the end of which are several fibers. Inside the head there is a single coil of DNA. The phage is about one one-hundred-thousandth of an inch long, and about 1,000 phages can fit nicely into a single colon bacterium.

A single phage attaches itself to a bacterium by means of its tail fibers, and with the help of enzymes it bores a hole through the thick wall of its victim. The tail then contracts and the phage shoots its DNA thread into the bacterial cell in the manner of a hypodermic needle. The head and tail remain outside the cell and only the DNA thread enters. Once inside, the virus DNA takes over the chemical machinery of the bacterial cell like an invading dictator and converts it to its own use. The first step in this "take-over" is to destroy the control center of the cell, the DNA of the bacterium itself. The virus makes enzymes which crumble the bacterial DNA to pieces. The captured cell now works for the DNA of the virus. It continues to take in food, produce energy, and make proteins, but under the directions and supervision of the conqueror. Virus DNA orders the vanquished cell to make more viruses instead of bacterial parts. Within minutes, several hundred new virus DNA threads are assembled, replicas of the invading DNA. The cell also constructs protein coats, copies of the original virus coat, to fit the virus DNA threads. Ten minutes after the virus first enters the cell, the new DNA threads begin to slip into their new protein outfits. Thirty minutes after the invasion, some 300 new fully clad viruses pack an empty bacterial cell. They then crash through the wall with the help of enzymes leaving an empty shell behind. Each virus is now ready to inject its deadly DNA coil into another bacterium and duplicate itself until all the bacteria are destroyed.

Virus Coats and Coils

How did scientists prove that invading phages leave their coats outside? A most elegant experiment in 1952 by Alfred D. Hershey and Martha Chase, working at the Cold Spring Harbor Genetics Laboratory of the Carnegie Institute, proved that only the DNA of the virus enters and reproduces inside the bacterial cell. They tagged the protein coat of the virus with radioactive sulfur and the

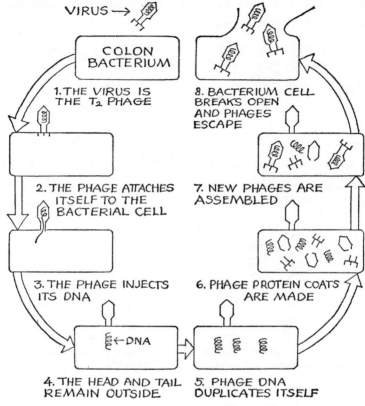

VIRUS →

COLON BACTERIUM

1. THE VIRUS IS THE T₂ PHAGE

8. BACTERIUM CELL BREAKS OPEN AND PHAGES ESCAPE

2. THE PHAGE ATTACHES ITSELF TO THE BACTERIAL CELL

7. NEW PHAGES ARE ASSEMBLED

3. THE PHAGE INJECTS ITS DNA

6. PHAGE PROTEIN COATS ARE MADE

←DNA

4. THE HEAD AND TAIL REMAIN OUTSIDE

5. PHAGE DNA DUPLICATES ITSELF

Virus DNA duplication inside a bacterium

DNA coil with radioactive phosphorus. Since sulfur is present only in the protein and not in the DNA, and phosphorus is limited to the DNA and absent from the protein, the fate of these tagged parts can be followed along the invasion route. After the phage invades the bacterium, the phosphorus appears only inside the cell and the sulfur is restricted to the outside. Here was proof that only the

DNA enters the bacterial cell and it alone displays the powers of reproduction.

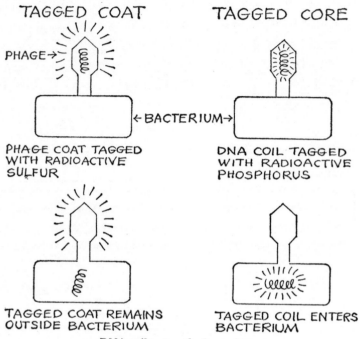

TAGGED COAT   TAGGED CORE

PHAGE→

←BACTERIUM→

PHAGE COAT TAGGED
WITH RADIOACTIVE
SULFUR

DNA COIL TAGGED
WITH RADIOACTIVE
PHOSPHORUS

TAGGED COAT REMAINS
OUTSIDE BACTERIUM

TAGGED COIL ENTERS
BACTERIUM

DNA coil enters the bacterium

DNA Duplication—Two from One

A most challenging question being studied by scientists is how the DNA molecules are able to make such accurate copies of themselves. Let us take another look at the Crick-Watson model, since it suggests a very simple mechanism for DNA duplication. As we have already seen, DNA has the shape of a twisted ladder the two sides of which are long chains of alternating sugar and phosphate units held together by connecting rungs. The rungs contain pairs of bases joined by hydrogen bonds; A in one chain is coupled with T in the second chain or vice versa and the C with G, or G with C. Thus A is always paired with T, and C with G.

Crick and Watson believe that DNA duplication occurs by a process in which the twisted ladder splits down the middle and each half assembles a complete ladder. They think that first the DNA ladder begins to untwist and the hydrogen bonds holding the base pairs together break in orderly succession starting at one end. In effect, the ladder straightens out and unzips lengthwise through the middle of each rung, thus separating the bases. The members of each pair of bases are now exposed to the cytoplasm, the cell's sea, which contains the molecular building blocks for DNA as well as other raw materials of life. Each base in the half ladder is now free to pick up a new molecular mate from the cytoplasm. However, these chemical matings are limited. For example, A in the chain can join up only with a free T, since these two bases fit together perfectly. Free C and G bases will be rejected by A because they do not match. Similarly, G in the chain hooks up with a free C base or the reverse. The newly attached bases pick up the sugar and phosphate units to complete the ladder. In effect, each base latches on to a new partner exactly like its previous one. The new units are in precisely the same place and in the same order as the old ones.

Finally, when the splitting and the pairing processes are completed, two DNA molecules stand in the place of one.

Each of the two halves in the original DNA molecule has assembled a new half which is exactly like the old one. Instead of one ladder, there are two ladders, each containing one original and one new chain. The resulting DNA molecules are identical with the original mother molecule. When the cell reproduces, each daughter cell receives DNA molecules in the same amount and of the same kind as those in the original cell.

One Old, One New

How do we know that DNA ladders make other ladders like themselves by first splitting and then each half building a full one?

A sophisticated experiment to answer this question was devised by Meselson and Stahl in 1958, using bacteria grown on food enriched with heavy nitrogen, N-15. They succeeded in raising a population of bacteria in which both strands of the DNA molecules in them were tagged with N-15. These tagged bacteria were then put on a diet containing ordinary nitrogen N-14 and permitted to reproduce for two successive generations. After the first division, the DNA content of these organisms was analyzed and found to be half N-15 and half N-14. After the second division, two kinds of DNA appeared; one was all N-14 and the other half N-15 and half N-14.

These findings are in complete accord with the Crick-Watson explanation of DNA duplication. At the first division, the two N-15 strands of DNA separated and each became the mold for assembling a new strand from the

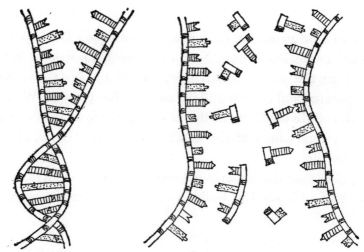

1. DNA LADDER UNTWISTS
AND UNZIPS THROUGH THE
MIDDLE OF EACH PAIR OF
BASES

2. EACH BASE IN EACH HALF
LADDER PICKS UP A NEW
MOLECULAR MATE FROM
CYTOPLASM

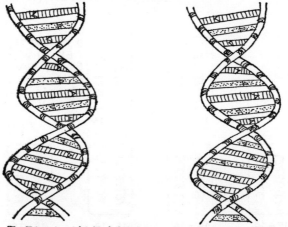

3. EACH HALF LADDER ASSEMBLES A NEW
PARTNER EXACTLY LIKE ITS PREVIOUS
ONE, TWO NEW LADDERS ARE FORMED,
IDENTICAL WITH THE ORIGINAL

DNA duplication—two from one

N-14 food around it. Each daughter cell got a DNA molecule consisting of one N-15 and one N-14 strand. Just
before the next cell division, the N-14 : N-15 strands
separated and each assembled another N-14 strand. When
this cell divided, one of the new cells received the N-15 :
N-14 molecule and the other cell got the N-14 : N-14
molecule.

How does this experiment show that DNA ladders split
in half and each half builds a new one? When the tagged

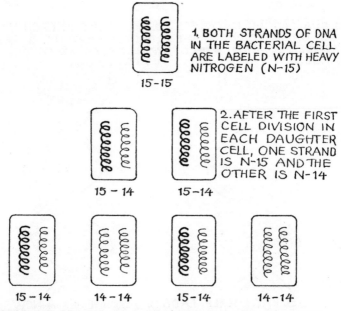

1. BOTH STRANDS OF DNA
IN THE BACTERIAL CELL
ARE LABELED WITH HEAVY
NITROGEN (N-15)

15-15

2. AFTER THE FIRST
CELL DIVISION IN
EACH DAUGHTER
CELL, ONE STRAND
IS N-15 AND THE
OTHER IS N-14

15 - 14   15 -14

15 - 14   14 - 14   15 - 14   14 -14

3. AFTER THE SECOND CELL DIVISION, THE DNA STRANDS
ARE N-15/N-14 IN HALF THE CELLS AND N-14/N-14
IN THE OTHER HALF

DNA duplication takes place with each cell division

ladders split, this resulted in two tagged half ladders. These then built untagged halves, so that each of the ladders was half tagged and half untagged. These half-and-half type ladders then split and again each half built another untagged half. This time two kinds of ladder appeared. One type was half tagged and half untagged; in the other kind both halves were untagged.

Duplicating Tagged Chromosomes

Before a cell divides, each chromosome duplicates itself and appears as a pair of short rods lying side by side. When the cell divides, the pairs separate and one chromosome of each pair goes to each of the daughter cells. Thus, each new cell contains copies of each of the original chromosomes. A question that arises is "How is the reproduction of the chromosomes related to the reproduction of the DNA in it?" Another experiment similar to that with bacteria tested the template theory of DNA duplication in terms of chromosome duplication.

In 1957, J. Herbert Taylor of Columbia University in New York City, working with Walter L. Hughes and Philip S. Woods of Brookhaven National Laboratory, attempted to find an answer to this question by following the fate of tagged DNA through successive divisions of the chromosomes in the cells of a bean plant. When cells are grown in a solution containing thymidine, which is one of the constituents of DNA, the thymidine is taken up only by the chromosomes and the DNA in them, since no other part of the cell uses it. Now if this molecule is tagged with

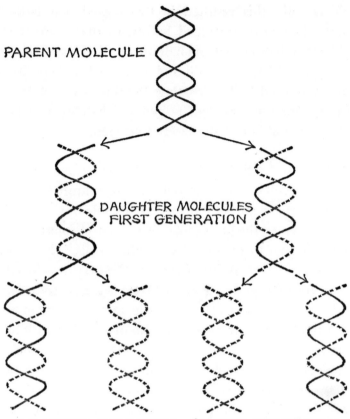

PARENT MOLECULE

DAUGHTER MOLECULES
FIRST GENERATION

DAUGHTER MOLECULES – SECOND GENERATION

DNA ladders split and each half builds a new ladder

tritium, a radioactive form of hydrogen, it can be traced
into the chromosomes and through their successive divisions. The rays emitted by tritium travel a very short distance, and when they strike a photographic plate, dark
spots are produced, pinpointing the exact location of

DNA in the chromosome. Although a tagged chromosome cannot be distinguished from an untagged one by the human eye, photographic film can "tell" them apart. This technique is called radioautography (radio-aw-TOG-ra-fee) because molecules tagged with radioactive atoms take pictures of themselves on photographic film.

The roots of bean plants were grown in a solution of tagged thymidine for a few hours. Taylor then removed a few of the bean cells, squashed them under a plate of glass and covered it with a thin sheet of photographic film. The radioactive rays produced a photograph showing where the thymidine was concentrated. The radioautographs or pictures showed that all the chromosomes in the cell were tagged and the radioactive molecules were equally distributed. The plants were now taken out of the radioactive solution and placed in a solution of non-radioactive thymidine. After these labeled chromosomes had reproduced, some of the cells were again squashed under glass and covered by film. This time photographs showed that in each of the paired chromosomes, one was tagged and one was not.

Taylor explained this meant that a chromosome consists of two parts or strands, each of which acts as a mold or template. When the cells were in the radioactive solution, each pair of chromosomes, after splitting in two, assembled a new radioactive mate. All the new chromosomes contained one tagged and one untagged strand. When transferred to the non-radioactive solution, each of these strands formed untagged mates. Hence half the chromo-

somes were tagged and half were not. This is exactly what
happened in the experiment with bacteria.

These findings are consistent with what is known about
the DNA molecule and the Crick-Watson theory. The
DNA molecule contains two chains twisted around one
another. When they duplicate, the chains unwind and
each builds itself a new partner. The chromosomes also
seem to contain two chains which separate, and each serves
as a template for assembling a new partner. We still do not
know how DNA molecules are arranged in the chromosomes.

Man-made DNA

One of the most exciting experiments supporting the
ladder-splitting, ladder-building theory of DNA duplication came from efforts to make DNA in a test tube. In
1957 Dr. Arthur Kornberg of the Washington University
in St. Louis startled the scientific world by his successful
synthesis of DNA outside the cell. During his first at-
tempt, he mixed the six submolecular pieces of DNA—
sugar, phosphate, and four bases—with some other chemicals including an enzyme needed to put the pieces together. The results were very disappointing; only a tiny
bit of DNA-like substance was formed.

To act as a primer or starter, Kornberg now added a
speck of DNA extracted from an intestinal bacterium.
This time there was no question about the reaction—the
six basic building blocks were linked into chains of DNA.
The most astonishing thing about this test-tube DNA was

its resemblance to the bacterial DNA that had been added as a primer. Kornberg now obtained DNA extracts from another kind of bacterium, from a virus and from a cow. He added these separately to his mixture. In each case, DNA turned up, and in each case the DNA formed was a replica of the primer DNA. It appears that even in a test tube DNA acted as a mold or template for assembling new molecules in its own chemical image.

The Kornberg-created DNA was the exact replica of natural DNA chemically as well as physically. However, it lacked one thing—it was not alive. It did not reproduce or do all the other things DNA can do. Kornberg's efforts brought us much closer to the possibility of creating life in a test tube, that is, making a molecule that not only looks like DNA but acts like DNA. For his synthesis of DNA, Kornberg shared the 1959 Nobel Prize with Dr. Severo Ochoa of New York University, who succeeded in making RNA molecules in a test tube.

6

Proteins Unlimited

DNA works its wonders by commanding the production of molecules. Most important are molecules of protein. DNA contains detailed instructions which are sent to the cell for making a rich assortment of these molecules. DNA is the expert designer of proteins and the cell the expert producer of them.

Proteins are huge, complex molecules essential for life. The very word *protein* means "primary, holding first place," which is precisely the position these molecules occupy in the scheme of life. All living things, from the smallest to the largest, contain these vital molecules. They are the major molecules in the structure of the cell. The membrane, cytoplasm, and nucleus are composed of proteins.

Proteins at Work

Every living part of your body has some kind of protein in it. Half the dry weight of your body is made of tens of thousands of different proteins. They are part of your skin, hair, nails, muscles, tendons, ligaments, bones, and blood. Proteins are the chief molecular building blocks of life.

Enzymes are proteins that trigger practically every chemical reaction associated with life. Teams of enzymes digest your food, oxidize it, capture and transfer energy, and also assist in building molecules such as DNA, RNA, and other proteins. An individual cell may contain as many as 1,000 different enzymes, each promoting one of the hundreds of high-speed chemical reactions taking place in every cell of your body each second of your life.

The chemical activities of living things are coordinated by another group of proteins, the hormones (HORE-moans). In animals, these chemical coordinators are manufactured by special glands which secrete their hormones directly into the bloodstream. For example, the thyroid gland (THIGH-royd) in your neck produces the hormone thyroxin (thigh-ROCK-sin), which regulates the rate of oxidation in your body, that is, how fast the "flame" of life burns. The pituitary (pit-TYOU-ih-ter-ee) gland located at the base of the brain makes about twenty different hormones, many of which regulate the other hormone-producing glands.

Proteins known as antibodies are the chemical defenders of the body. They guard you against germs and the diseases germs cause. The polio germ stimulates your body to make specific polio antibodies which protect you against this disease only. Organisms have an almost limitless capacity to produce antibodies, each specific for a particular germ or its poison. In general, proteins determine our form and function, that is, what we are and what we do.

Mammoth Molecules

Proteins are the largest and most complex molecules found in living things. These molecules always contain the chemical elements—carbon, oxygen, hydrogen, and nitrogen. Sulfur is usually present as well as some other elements. Compared to most molecules, proteins are enormous. Hemoglobin, the oxygen-carrying molecule in your blood, is an average-size protein containing 10,000 atoms. Of these, 3,000 are carbon, 5,000 hydrogen, close to 900 oxygen, approximately 800 nitrogen, 8 sulfur, and 4 iron. Insulin, the hormone that controls sugar metabolism in your body, is a tiny molecule with only 777 atoms.

Protein Building Blocks—Amino Acids

Proteins are composed of chains of submolecular units called amino acids. There may be as few as eight or as many as 100,000 of these building blocks in a protein molecule. About twenty kinds of amino acids occur commonly in proteins and they are used repeatedly as structural units. Hence, instead of six kinds of building blocks —sugar, phosphate and four bases—as in DNA, protein may have as many as twenty varieties of amino **acids**, which may appear in innumerable combination. The tiny insulin molecule contains a total of 51 submolecular units, but there are only 17 different kinds of amino acids included. Hemoglobin, the average-size protein, consists of 600 amino acids which fall into 19 varieties.

Amino acids are very much alike in chemical structure. They all have the same atomic backbone, a short chain of two carbon atoms and one nitrogen atom —C—C—N—.

NAME	GENERAL FORMULA	GLYCINE	ALANINE	CYSTINE	
SAME ATOMS	H O H H O-C-C-N-H	H O H H O-C-C-N-H	H O H H O-C-C-N-H	H O H H O-C-C-N-H	H O H H O-C-C-N-H
DIFFERENT ATOMS	R	H	H-C-H , H	H-C-H S————	H-C-H S

Amino acids are very much alike in chemical structure

Each amino acid can be thought of as a railroad car with a pair of couplings, one in front and one in the rear. Just as railroad cars are hooked on to another to make a train, so amino acids are linked end to end to make long chains of these units —C—C—N— —C—C—N— —C—C—N—. The nitrogen atom of one amino acid can be hooked on to the carbon of the neighboring unit.

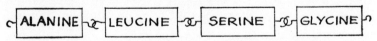

Amino acids are linked end to end, forming chains

Amino Acids in Chains

Coming back to the example of the railroad train, any

kind of car can be coupled with another car—a flat car,
a box car, a tank car, a passenger car, or a caboose—and
they can be joined in any order. Similarly, any number of
amino acids can be linked, and in any order. However,
each arrangement of these amino acids gives you a different protein. Whenever you change the order of these units
you change the protein.

How many different combinations of amino acids are
possible in a protein? The number of kinds of proteins
that can be made from the twenty kinds of amino acids is
beyond belief. This becomes more evident if you think
of the amino acids as letters and the proteins as the words
in this twenty-letter alphabet. You have only to thumb
through the pages of a dictionary to appreciate the number of English words that can be made with a twenty-six-
letter alphabet, and most of these are relatively short
words with less than ten letters. Now add the words in the
French, German, Spanish, and Swedish dictionaries and
you will have some idea of the number of proteins that
can be formed.

In the chemical language of proteins, the letters may
be in any order and the words of any length. The average
"word" contains 300 of these "letters." For example, a
chain of five different amino acids can be arranged in 120
different combinations. By doubling the number of amino
acids in the chain to ten, the combination possibilities are
increased to $3\frac{1}{2}$ million. In a chain of twenty amino acids,
one of each kind, the number of different sequences is
greater than the total population of life on earth. How

many possible combinations do you think there are in the average protein of 500 amino acids? The number is greater than the total number of atoms in the universe.

Protein Profiles

What is the structure of protein molecules? Scientists are interested in the architecture of these molecules, since they believe that what proteins can do depends upon how they are built. Each kind of protein seems to be especially designed for its particular task. A protein may consist of a single twisted chain of amino acids, or a bundle of twisted chains, or fibers bound together. To illustrate, the insulin molecule contains two chains, a long one with thirty amino acids and a short one with twenty-one. Ligaments which hold together the bones of the body and tendons which attach muscles to the bones, both consist of bundles of coiled fibers bound together like cable wires. There are some proteins in which the chains are folded back and forth into loops and coils assuming the general shape of a ball. Many hormones, as well as hemoglobin and enzymes, have this globular shape.

The first real breakthrough in deciphering the general

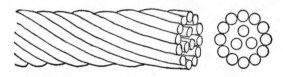

A protein may consist of a bundle of fibers resembling a cable

shape of a protein molecule was announced in 1950 by Linus Pauling and Robert B. Corey at the California Institute of Technology. Using X-ray diffractions, they located the exact position and calculated the precise distance between the atoms in an amino acid molecule. They came to the conclusion that the amino acids do not follow one another in a straight line but are twisted into spiral or coiled chains. For tracking down the shape of a protein molecule, Pauling was awarded the Nobel Prize in 1954.

The second important advance was determining the exact sequence of the amino acids in the protein chain. This feat was first achieved at Cambridge University in England by Frederick Sanger and his associates, who spent ten years studying the "tiny" insulin molecule. Not only did he discover the general shape of this molecule but, more important, he worked out the precise sequence of the fifty-one amino acids in its two twisted chains. As a reward for disclosing for the first time the internal structure of a protein which is described as the "most complicated of all substances occurring in nature," Sanger received the Nobel Prize in 1958.

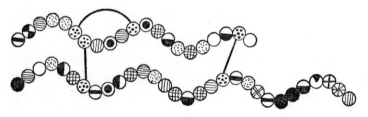

The insulin molecule

Six years later, in 1964, the first man-made protein was produced. A group of scientists at the University of Pittsburgh announced the synthesis of insulin.

The third and most recent front in which advances have been made in obtaining a complete picture of proteins is its three-dimensional structure. The way in which chains of amino acids are bent and folded in space has been worked out for the first time by two British scientists. In 1962, when Crick, Watson, and Wilkins were awarded Nobel Prizes in Physiology and Medicine for their 3-D model of DNA, Dr. Max Perutz and Dr. John C. Kendrew, both of the Laboratory of Molecular Biology in Cambridge, England, were honored in Chemistry for their 3-D models of protein molecules. Kendrew made a scale model of myoglobin (MY-oh-glow-bin), the protein in muscle, and Perutz exhibited the fantastically complicated molecular model of hemoglobin with its 10,000 atoms.

X-ray Picture of Protein Molecules

The exact position of the atoms in myoglobin and hemoglobin was located by firing X rays at them and obtaining "shadow pictures" in much the same way as Wilkins had done with DNA. After many years and thousands and thousands of X-ray pictures, the atoms were located and accurate scale models of these proteins could be constructed. To their amazement, Kendrew and Perutz found an astonishing similarity between these molecules. Hemoglobin contains four similar chains of amino acids

and each of these bears a great resemblance to myoglobin.
This was surprising since the proteins in this investigation
not only came from different animals but also from different parts of the body, the myoglobin from the sperm whale
muscle and the hemoglobin from horse blood. In both
instances, the molecules are a maze of interconnecting
threads bent into a very intricate and elaborate three-dimensional pattern. But this was not the end of surprises.
They found that the threads in each of these molecules
are twisted in the shape of a coil. Two of the basic materials of life, DNA and proteins, are coiled threads, DNA
a double thread and proteins a single one.

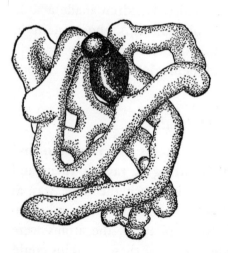

The myoglobin molecule
*Adaptation courtesy of Dr.
Kendrew*

And so protein molecules differ from one another in
the number, sequence, and spatial arrangement of the
amino acids. The number of proteins that can be created

from twenty amino acids is sufficient for every conceivable purpose in every living thing. But the kinds of proteins in each individual organism seem to be fixed and this we believe is set by the genetic message.

7

DNA and the Genetic Code of Life

The DNA molecule dictates the making of blond hair, or blue eyes, or any one of the thousands of traits that you have. How?

At this very moment scientists are trying to find answers to this question by learning how to "read" the genetic information contained in the DNA molecule. They are on the verge of "cracking" the genetic code and disclosing the secret of heredity locked up in the DNA molecule. They are attempting to discover how this molecule can be coded to make a man or a mouse, a fish or a fern, a tree or a toad.

We already know that DNA is a duplicating molecule that can make a replica of itself to pass on to the next generation. The reproductive cells, sperm and egg, split off from the parent organism and contain parent DNA. At fertilization the microscopic sperm, containing the DNA of the male parent, enters the egg which holds the DNA of the female parent. The fertilized egg now contains packets of DNA from both parents and it is this combination of molecules that controls the heredity of the offspring. In this way, DNA molecules are transmitted from one generation to the next and the traits of the parents are inherited by the children.

Blueprints of Life

The DNA in each organism contains thousands of specific messages which the cell "understands" and "obeys." It is believed that the genetic messages contain directions for making proteins. These vital molecules, you will recall, are composed of chains of amino acids, of which there are twenty common varieties. A typical protein contains a few hundred amino acids linked together in a very specific order. DNA supplies the instructions to the cell for placing each amino acid in its proper place along the protein chain.

Living "Punch Card"

The information in DNA is written in code that scientists are just learning to "read" and understand. This code can be compared to the Morse code, the dot-dash language used in telegraphic communication. If I say to you "dash-dot-dot dash-dot dot-dash," it has no meaning unless you know the Morse code. If you do, then you know the message reads "DNA." Similarly, the arrangement of the holes punched into cards fed into a computing machine means nothing to you. They do not give you any information. However, the number and the position of these holes are code symbols. When the cards are put into a computer, the pattern of these holes "tells" the machine what to do. The machine can "read" these symbols, follow the instructions, and translate them into words that you can read.

How is genetic information carried in DNA? The DNA molecules are the "punch cards" of life. The information they contain is in their molecular pattern just as the information on a punch card is in the pattern of the holes in the card. According to the Crick-Watson model, DNA has the shape of a twisted ladder with rungs containing only four kinds of base pairs: A-T, T-A, C-G, and G-C. The DNA in your body, in a cow, in a blade of grass, and in a virus, all has the same general molecular structure. The differences are in the *order* of the base pairs in the rungs of the ladder. The sequence of the bases along the DNA ladder spells out the genetic message and each species carries its own particular base sequence. In fact, except for identical twins, which are derived from the same fertilized egg, no two individuals have the same order of bases in their DNA. This is another way of saying that each organism has its own particular genetic message which makes it different from all other living things.

The Four-letter Genetic Alphabet

The symbols in the DNA molecule are the four bases found in the rungs of this ladder of life. Each base pair represents a different code letter. All the words and sentences contained in a genetic message are written in this four-letter alphabet of life.

Keeping the bases in a given order is as important in conveying genetic information as the correct sequence of letters in a word. If you shift the letters in CAT to ACT, the entire meaning of the word is changed. Altering the sequence of bases in DNA changes the genetic messages and the nature of the organism, perhaps from brown hair to no hair at all.

In a DNA molecule with just a few hundred base pairs, the number of different ways in which these pairs can be arranged is greater than the number of grains of sand in all the deserts of the world. The four-letter coded alphabet is sufficient for writing the fantastic amount of genetic information found in the ten billion base pairs of the DNA in your cells. There seems to be no practical limitation to the number of ways in which these four symbols can be arranged to write out a different genetic story for each living thing. This is not too surprising when you remember that the Morse code has only two symbols, a dot and a dash, and that the computer also operates on only two symbols.

If you could unwind a coil of DNA, magnify it a few million times and then read it, you could probably identify the organism from the sequence of base pairs, which you will recall are adenine (A), guanine (G), thymine (T), and cytosine (C). This information would probably read like data on a ticker tape. Taking the names of the bases on only one side of the ladder, the beginning of the genetic code for one strand of a butterfly's DNA might read:

ACC TGC ATC.

That of a baboon might read:

ACC TTT CGG.

Three-Letter Code Words

DNA "speaks" only in three-letter words, that is, three pairs of bases in sequence. It sends messages to the cells consisting exclusively of words containing any three of the four letters in the genetic alphabet—A, C, T, and G. These code letters can be combined into sixty-four different three-letter code words such as:

AAA AAG AAT AAC

GAA GAG GAT GAC

CAA CAG CAT CAC

There are fifty-two other code words. How many of these can you make? The genetic code contains sixty-four different words and all hereditary messages are written in this language of life.

Reading the Code

How should the genetic message be read? Scientists think that each one of the twenty different kinds of amino acids is coded by a three-letter word, and that a string of these words constitutes the genetic instructions for assembling a particular protein. For example, the message

ACCAATAGAGGG is an instruction for making a protein containing four amino acids. The message should be read as a sentence containing four 3-letter words—ACC AAT AGA GGG. The first word ACC is the code word for one kind of amino acid—*a*, the second word AAT is the code word for another amino acid—*b*, the third word AGA is the code combination for amino acid *c*, and the fourth word GGG is for amino acid *d*. The decoded message reads: "Make a protein consisting of amino acids *a-b-c-d*, and in that order."

Cracking the Code

How did scientists find out which code word stood for which amino acid? How was the genetic code broken? A most startling and spectacular breakthrough in cracking the genetic code came in 1961 when Dr. Marshall W. Nirenberg and Dr. J. Heinrich Matthaei, both working at the National Institute of Health in Bethesda, Maryland, successfully deciphered one of the sixty-four words. They used a molecule of RNA, a chemical cousin and close collaborator of DNA, consisting entirely of one of the four bases normally present in this molecule—uracil—which we shall represent by the letter U. This molecule called Poly U was put in a test tube with the protein-making machinery which they extracted from a living cell. Cells were broken open by gently grinding them with a fine powder. The cell sap released from these ruptured cells was still able to make proteins. They now added a mixture of all the amino acids. The protein-pro-

ducing machinery set Poly U in operation and a protein
turned up in the test tube. Nirenberg and Matthaei got
a protein consisting of only one kind of amino acid, phenylalanine (FEN-ill-AL-uh-neen). Although all the other
nineteen amino acids were present and available, Poly U
chose only the phenylalanine molecules and wove them
into a protein chain. There was no doubt that the genetic
code word for phenylalanine was UUU. Thus, the first
word to be placed in the genetic code book was UUU
meaning phenylalanine in the language of life.

More Code Words

Poly U quickly became the wedge for uncovering more
code words. Dr. Severo Ochoa, who won the Nobel Prize
in 1959 for synthesizing RNA, together with his group,
joined forces with Nirenberg and Matthaei and together
they launched an all-out attack on the genetic code. They
made RNA molecules with more than uracil and began to
decipher other code words. At present, the letters in the
code words for all of the twenty amino acids are known.
However, there are difficulties arranging the letters in
their proper order in some of these words. Genetic coding
is like a game of anagrams—you may know all the letters
but not the order in which they must be arranged if they
are to form words. If CAT are the three letters in the code
word for a particular amino acid, they can also spell ACT,
TAC, TCA, and CTA. Which one is the correct spelling
of the code word for a particular protein?

Can you read the coded message that follows?

Code:

AAA	D
CCC	O
TTT	R
AGA	N
CAA	L
ATA	E
AGG	I
CAT	F
GAC	A

Message:

CAA GAC AAA AAA ATA TTT
L   A   D   D   E   R
CCC CAT CAA AGG CAT ATA
O   F   L   I   F   E
AAA AGA GAC
D   N   A

Universal Language of Life

Is the genetic code the universal language of life or does the DNA in different organisms "speak" different languages?

The question is being answered by seeing how the protein-making machinery of one kind of organism responds to the genetic message of another kind. Nirenberg and Matthaei, working with Fraenkel-Conrat, mixed the protein-making machinery of a bacterium in a test tube with the RNA of the tobacco mosaic virus (TMV). Would the protein-making machinery of the bacterium "understand" the genetic message contained in the RNA of the virus? The protein manufactured was like that present in the virus and not usually made by the bacterium. Apparently the genetic message in a virus is written in a language "understood" by a bacterium. This would seem to indicate that the genetic code is universal, the same for all organisms.

8

DNA, RNA, and Protein Production

The way in which DNA controls protein production brings us back to the cell. The DNA plans for the proteins are packed into chromosomes which remain inside the nucleus at all times. The actual *production* of proteins, however, takes place outside the nucleus, in the ribosomes, the protein-making centers of the cell, which are situated in the cytoplasm. The raw materials—the amino acids—needed by the ribosomes for manufacturing proteins are supplied largely by the foods you eat. The enzymes in your digestive system split the proteins in the food you eat into amino acids, which are eventually distributed to the cells of your body. There DNA organizes these food units into the many kinds of proteins needed by the body. Thus the DNA in your cells takes the amino acids which came from cow protein in the form of a steak, and reassembles them to make human proteins. How is this done?

RNA—Molecular Messenger of DNA

How can DNA, which is restricted to the nucleus, control a process going on in the cytoplasm? What is the link between DNA and the ribosome? The gap between the plan and the protein is bridged by molecules of RNA, ribonucleic acid, which is a first chemical cousin to DNA. There is a continuous flow of instructions from the master planner, DNA via RNA, the master contractor, to the master builder, the ribosome. RNA molecules transmit the genetic messages to the protein factories; they tell the ribosomes the kinds and quantities of proteins to produce. RNA is directly involved in the protein-making business of the cell.

There are many reasons for regarding RNA as the molecular messenger of DNA. In a cell, DNA is present only in the nucleus, whereas approximately 90% of the RNA is located in the ribosomes of the cytoplasm. In addition, delicate techniques have detected the nucleus in the act of discharging bits of RNA into the cytoplasm.

All cells contain RNA but some more than others. Cells which produce large amounts of proteins contain large amounts of RNA. Growing cells have more RNA than resting cells, because growth involves increasing their protein content. The cells of the pancreas and liver, which are constantly making and secreting proteins such as enzymes and hormones, are very rich in RNA.

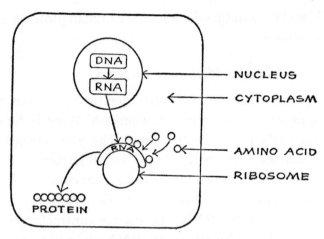

DNA—RNA and protein production

RNA—Half a DNA Ladder

An excellent reason for thinking that RNA carries out the instructions of DNA is the chemical and physical resemblances between them. Both are composed of six submolecular pieces. However, instead of looking like a twisted ladder with two strands connected by rungs, RNA is generally thought to look like half of a twisted ladder. The single strand, which is the backbone of the molecule, consists of alternating sugar and phosphate units. The sugar in RNA is ribose, which has one more oxygen atom in its molecule than deoxyribose of DNA. There are four bases connected to the sugar units, three of which are identical with those found in DNA—adenine (A), guanine (G), and cytosine (C). The fourth RNA base is uracil (U) in place of thymine (T) in DNA. RNA looks like a DNA molecule which has been cut lengthwise through the rungs.

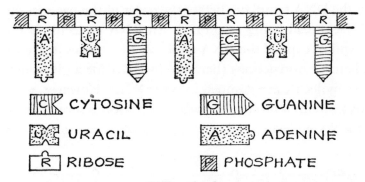

CYTOSINE   GUANINE

URACIL   ADENINE

RIBOSE   PHOSPHATE

RNA molecule

Recent X-ray diffraction pictures of RNA, although not as clear or as definite as those of DNA, suggest that, in some instances, at least part of the molecule is a double thread. By looping back on itself, the matching bases in one part of the strand can link up with the matching bases in the other part and appear as a partially double threaded structure.

Making RNA Molecules

How is genetic information for making proteins transferred from DNA to RNA? DNA makes a molecule in its own chemical image specifically for this purpose. In all likelihood a segment of the DNA molecule unwinds and one of its strands serves as a template or mold for lining up the proper chemical along its length. The process is very much like that in DNA duplication except, as previously indicated, the chain being assembled contains uracils (U), in place of thymines (T), and ribose instead of deoxyribose. The A, C, G, and T bases in the DNA template pick up U, C, G, and A respectively. The sequence of the bases in the DNA template dictate the order of the bases in the RNA thread being assembled. An RNA molecule is the chemical copy of the DNA molecule that makes it. Hence whatever instructions there are in DNA for a given protein molecule are stamped into the RNA. However, making proteins is no simple matter and requires several kinds of RNA molecules, all of which are DNA creations.

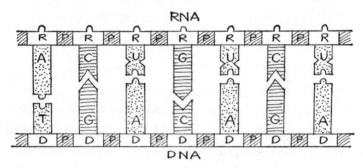

How DNA makes RNA

Messenger RNA

One kind of RNA carries messages from the DNA in the nucleus to the ribosome; it is appropriately called "messenger" RNA. Each "messenger" has imprinted on it a copy of the instructions in the DNA for making one specific kind of protein. Therefore, there are as many kinds of these RNA molecules as there are proteins in that living thing. Messenger RNA molecules pass into the cytoplasm and attach themselves to the ribosomes. Here they, in turn, become the templates or molds on which amino acids are assembled, in an order dictated by the sequence of the bases in messenger RNA. The ribosome is now keyed to assemble the proteins for which it has received instructions. Until the ribosome is supplied with the proper instructions, it can do nothing—it is an idle factory. However, these factories can produce many kinds of proteins, depending upon the instructions they receive through messenger RNA.

Transfer RNA—Code-Reading Molecule

DNA creates another kind of RNA molecule for the express purpose of picking up specific amino acids from the cytoplasm and bringing them to their proper place on the messenger RNA assembly line in the ribosome. There are at least twenty kinds of "transfer" RNA molecules, one for each kind of amino acid. Each kind of transfer RNA molecule latches on to a particular amino acid and brings it to a specific spot on the template. How does a transfer RNA molecule "recognize" a given amino acid and also how does it "know" where to place it on the ribosome assembly line? There is some evidence that one end of all transfer RNA molecules carries the same three-letter code word but is able to recognize a particular amino acid and also to hook on to it. The other end of the transfer molecule is also thought to be coded, but only for "recognizing" its place on the RNA template.

As the various places on the messenger RNA template are filled with the correct amino acids, they join with one another, forming a protein chain. The transfer RNA molecules are set free to ferry more of the same amino acids from the cytoplasm to the ribosomal template. The

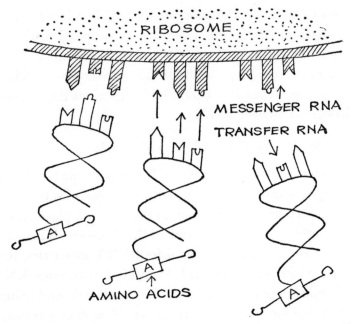

Transfer RNA molecules bring specific amino acids to messenger RNA template

newly made protein molecule peels off the template and goes to work in the life stream of the cell.

The entire process takes place in a matter of minutes. Dr. Richard Sweet of the University of Kentucky and Dr. Howard M. Dintzis of the Massachusetts Institute of Technology found that the amino acids making up hemoglobin are joined together in the ribosome in zipper-like fashion. Starting at one end of the chain, amino acids link up one after the other until the entire protein molecule is complete. It takes less than two minutes to hook together the 150 amino acids in the hemoglobin chains, at the rate of two per second.

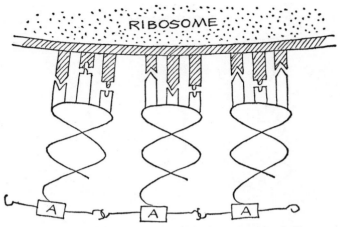

Amino acids join one another, forming a protein chain

From Gene to Protein

Thus the DNA molecules contain instructions for making proteins. The "blueprints" for each kind of protein are called genes. Each gene is located on a specific portion of DNA coil and the genes follow one another along the length of the DNA molecule like bits of information on a ticker tape.

In summary, DNA, the director of the cell, controls all cellular activities from the executive suite in the nucleus. The master plan for making thousands of proteins are filed in separate genes stored in the cell's filing cabinets, the chromosomes.

Being a good executive, DNA does not do all the work itself. It creates assistants and gives them responsibilities. These assistants are the various kinds of RNA molecules. One group of assistants is messenger RNA molecules, which are chemical copies of genes containing the blue-

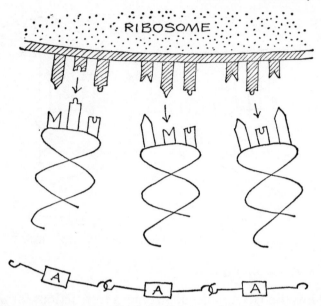

Newly made protein molecule peels off the template and goes to work in life stream of the cell

prints for making a specific protein. These molecules go out into the cytoplasm and "tell" the ribosomes, the protein-producing factories, what kind of protein to make. Another DNA creation is represented by transfer RNA molecules, which are coded to recognize and pick up specific loose amino acids and bring them to the proper place on the ribosomal assembly line. As the various amino acids take their places, they join in a chain forming the protein "ordered" in the chemical instructions contained in the gene. The newly formed protein slips off the assembly line, and the ribosome machinery is free to make more of the same protein, or is ready to receive a set of new instructions.

9

Mutations—Mistaken DNA Messages

There is, for the most part, a very strong resemblance between parents and their offspring. Baby zebras sport stripes just like their parents; young giraffes are as long-necked as their ancestors, and the hand of an infant is unmistakably human. However, every once in a while, a "freak" appears among a group of organisms, dramatically different from its parents and the other members of the species. White blackbirds, six-toed kittens, seedless apples, and wingless flies are examples of these "odd balls." In some instances, these "freaks" have offspring that also are "freaks." Such inherited changes are called mutations (mew-TAY-shuns) and individuals showing these unusual traits are referred to as mutants.

Mutations occur universally in all living things without exception. Normal five-fingered parents may have six-fingered children, and red bacteria may give rise to white ones. This tendency to be "different" is one of the characteristics of being alive; mutations are a built-in property of life.

Mutations—A Gene Change

Until the turn of the present century, there was no scientific explanation for these "freaks" which appear rarely but regularly in nature. Mutations seem to be mistakes or accidents of nature which disappear, with others always cropping up to take their place.

One day, about 1910, a "freak" suddenly appeared among the fruit flies being raised and studied by Thomas H. Morgan and his workers at Columbia University. They were conducting experiments in heredity, using a tiny fly commonly found around ripe fruit in the summer. This "freak" had white eyes in sharp contrast with the red eyes of its parents and of all other fruit flies. By breeding the white-eyed fly with normal red-eyed ones, Morgan created a new variety of white-eyed flies. What caused the mutation? Morgan examined the chromosomes of the mutants, hoping to find some differences between white- and red-eyed flies which would account for these mutations, but none could be detected. However, these mutations led to other studies and eventually to the modern chromosome theory of genetics, the idea that chromosomes consist of genes, units of heredity, which are arranged like beads on a string. In 1933, Morgan received the Nobel Prize for his "discoveries relating to the hereditary function of the chromosomes." Mutations were explained as changes in the genes, but nothing was then known about their chemical or physical structure.

Mutations—Mixed-up DNA

Today the gene is described as a portion or segment along the DNA ladder consisting of a set sequence of bases coded to produce a particular protein. Mutations are now defined as the result of changes in the order of the bases in the DNA molecules. DNA makes endless replicas of itself without error, like a printing press turning out copy. It duplicates the exact sequence of the thousands and millions of bases which represent the genetic code for thousands of traits. However, every once in a hundred thousand or million duplications, something goes wrong, and an error is made copying one or more of the bases. A base may be changed, or omitted, or put in the wrong place, or an extra one added. In any event, the genetic message is changed and a mutation may show up. For example, the base sequence in a normal five-fingered boy may read

ACG TTG CAT

while the copy may read

ACG TTG GAT

A "copy error" was made in reproducing the C in the last triplet and a G appeared instead. This may be the only difference in a chain of thousands of bases; it may change the entire meaning of the message and produce a six-fingered mutant. Once the "typographical" error creeps into the text of the DNA story and appears in the reproductive cells, the mutation is passed on to the off-spring.

Mutations Good and Bad

Since the discovery of the white-eyed mutation, hundreds of others have been found among fruit flies—flies without wings, without eyes, with yellow bodies instead of grey, and with purple eyes instead of red. Of course, only one fly in a hundred thousand or a million is a mutant. This may seem to make mutations a rare event. However, if you raise enough flies, mutations inevitably appear. The rate at which mutants show up depends upon the rate of reproduction of the species. Mutations appear more commonly in fruit flies than in humans because these flies produce a brood of a few hundred offspring every other week.

A very rich source of mutations for scientific investigation is found in viruses; they reproduce at the rate of ten times per minute.

NORMAL   MUTANT

One fruit fly in many hundred thousands is a mutant

Most mutations are "bad" for the organism; they put the mutant at a disadvantage in the struggle to survive. In nature, mutants rarely live long enough to reproduce;

they are killed off by their enemies. A wingless fly would probably not live very long in competition with its winged competitors for food and a mate. White-eyed female fruit flies prefer to mate with red-eyed males rather than with white-eyed males.

On the other hand, mutation can also be "good," giving an organism an advantage over its competitor. When this happens, the mutation survives and is passed on to more and more individuals in the species. The mutation that makes a bacterium resistant to penicillin is good for that kind of bacterium.

Whether a mutation is "good" or "bad" depends upon how it affects the life of an organism. In a stable environment, mutations rarely improve the organism. In a changing environment, the right mutation at the right time may save the species from being wiped out. The penicillin-resistant strain of bacteria is an excellent example of this. This is "good" for the bacterium, of course, but "bad" for a human being made sick by this organism.

From the very beginning of life about a billion or so years ago, mutations have been produced in an unending stream, and they are largely responsible for evolution. The millions of species of plants and animals which have appeared are the products of mutations which have accumulated in the DNA messages of these organisms and made them different. For the individual species, mutations are a kind of life insurance against a "rainy" day. It may never have to use the mutations but there is no way of knowing which one of the thousands of mutants appearing at random can save the species from extinction.

Molds and Mutations

The manner in which mutations affect an organism is most easily followed in simple living things, such as viruses, bacteria, and molds. This work was pioneered in the 1940's by George W. Beadle and Edward L. Tatum of Stanford University. They used the common pink mold, Neurospora (new-RAH-spo-ruh), which appears on bread in the summer. This mold can be grown in a test tube on a very simple diet consisting of a mixture of sulphate, phosphate, and nitrate salts, to which some table sugar and the vitamin biotin are added. From these few substances, neurospora can make amino acids, carbohydrates, proteins, fats, enzymes and all the vitamins, except biotin—in short, everything it needs in order to grow and reproduce.

The molds were exposed to X rays to induce mutations and then put back on their simple diet. Some of them could no longer grow on this diet. The X rays had altered some of the genes so that the mold could not make all the life-giving food substances. To find out exactly which substances the mutants could not synthesize, foods were added one by one until the mold began to grow.

For example, the X-rayed mold may have lost the power to make the vitamin niacin (NIGH-ah-sin), and therefore would not grow. When niacin was added to its diet, all was well again. Furthermore, when this disabled mold reproduced, all its offspring showed this same defect. The X-ray-induced mutation was inherited.

After performing hundreds of such experiments, Beadle

and Tatum came to the conclusion that genes control the chemical reactions in a living cell through enzymes, which, as we know, are protein molecules. They believe there is a specific gene for the synthesis of each enzyme taking part in the chemical reactions in the body. In 1958, Beadle and Tatum were awarded a share of the Nobel Prize for "their discoveries that genes act by regulating specific chemical reactions."

Mutation Makers in Nature

What causes mutations? What is there in nature that constantly upsets the DNA molecules in all living things and induces mutations? Actually, we do not know the causes of most of the natural mutations although we suspect many things around us. We know that the rate of mutations can be increased substantially by exposing reproductive cells to certain influences such as heat, chemicals, and radiation.

Everything on earth is constantly exposed to certain natural radiation: the cosmic rays from outer space, the ultra-violet rays of the sun, radioactive deposits, and now the latest addition, radioactive fallout from A-bomb testing. Cosmic rays, which constantly bombard the earth, are the most powerful and most penetrating particles of energy yet discovered. Every minute about eight of these rays pass through every square inch of your body. It is possible that as these particles shoot through a cell in your body, they hit a DNA molecule and knock off one or two atoms, thus changing the chemical composition of a base and altering the genetic message. If the target happens to be a sperm or an egg cell, then the mutation appears in the next generation.

Natural deposits of uranium and radium are distributed all over the world. The radiations given off by these radioactive minerals are capable of altering the DNA structure of an organism.

The atmosphere is full of radioactive particles dating back to the first atomic explosion in 1945. Most of these particles are quickly carried down to the earth by the rain and snow, while others remain suspended in air for years. As these radioactive particles rain down on us, they contaminate the air, soil and water. Plants and animals absorb them, and they enter your body in the food you eat, the water you drink, and the air you breathe. Once inside your body, some radioactive atoms continue giving off radiations for years and may cause mutations. Strontium 90, one of the radioactive fall-out atoms found in many foods and in water, tends to accumulate in the bones and it emits radiations for years. Its half-life is twenty-eight years, that is, it takes twenty-eight years for strontium 90 to lose half its radioactivity.

Man-made Radiation Mutations

It is no longer necessary to wait for nature to produce mutations. In 1927 Herman J. Muller, then at the University of Texas, discovered how to make mutations by exposing fruit flies to X rays. He was able to increase the natural mutation rate at least a hundred fold. The kinds of mutations he produced included some never seen before, while others were the same as those which appear naturally. For example, Muller found some white-eyed flies among his mutants; they looked and behaved exactly like the natural mutants. In 1946, Muller was awarded the Nobel Prize for his "discovery of the production of mutations by means of X-ray irradiations."

Muller could not make mutations "to order" nor predict what kind of mutations his X rays would produce. He was virtually shooting in the dark, hit or miss fashion. There is no way of aiming the X rays at a particular DNA molecule and hitting a particular gene. As the X rays pass through the cell, they fan out and strike anything in their path. Some, by chance, hit a chromosome and knock out or rearrange a few atoms in its DNA chain, thus changing the genetic message and producing a mutation.

Chemically Made Mutations

Many chemicals are capable of producing mutations. Recently a chemical has been found which can alter one of the bases in DNA and RNA, changing it into another nucleic acid base. Nitrous acid (HNO_2) transforms cytosine (C) into uracil (U). This is a very exciting and promising discovery since it provides a possible method for making mutations to "order." Fraenkel-Conrat treated naked RNA strands of the tobacco mosaic virus (TMV) with nitrous acid and rubbed them into tobacco leaves. A whole host of mutants of TMV appeared. When the protein coat assembled by the RNA of one of these mutants was compared with that of the parent virus, three out of the 158 amino acids making up the protein coats were different. Apparently, the nitrous acid, by changing a C to a U, had altered the triplet code word for some of the amino acids in the protein chain. Let us assume that CCA is the code word for the amino acid proline and that nitrous acid changed it to read UUC, which is the code word for another amino acid, leucine. We can then explain why a substitution of proline by leucine was one of the three replacements in the mutant protein coat.

Human Mutations

Human beings are not exempt from mutations. Some of the ills of humanity are the result of disturbed and disarranged DNA molecules. Hereditary diseases such as hemophilia and color-blindness are well known. Persons suffering from hemophilia are born with blood that clots with difficulty, if at all. Their chances of growing up to maturity are pretty slim since they can bleed to death from a cut or a scratch. Color-blind individuals are normal in every respect except one—they cannot tell the difference between red and green. Both these conditions are due to mutations.

In the past two decades, we have discovered hundreds of human diseases that have a genetic basis. Some are extremely rare but others are far more common than suspected. We shall now turn to a few of these genetic diseases.

10

DNA and Disease

In some of the malaria-ridden areas of Central Africa, almost half of the natives suffer from a most curious hereditary blood disease. The red cells in their blood stream have a perfectly normal disk shape in the lungs and arteries where oxygen is plentiful, but as soon as they pass into the capillaries and veins, which contain less oxygen, the cells collapse. Many of these red blood cells assume the shape of a curved knife blade or sickle and are therefore called sickle cells. The body destroys these defective and deformed sickle cells which seriously reduces the number of circulating red cells, causing a severe anemia. This disease, sickle-cell anemia (SCA), is fatal. It is caused by the mutation of a single gene. Persons suffering from SCA have two genes for sickling (SS); those with one gene for sickling and one for normal (SN) show no symptoms of the disease—they are "carriers"; and of course those with two genes for normal (NN) are perfectly healthy.

Misshapen Molecules

SCA has attracted considerable scientific attention because it is a "molecular disease" in which the mutation of a single gene alters the structure of a complex protein, hemoglobin, the oxygen-carrying substance in red cells. In 1958, Vernon M. Ingram and his associates at Cambridge University in England discovered the single change in the protein chain that completely alters the shape of the hemoglobin molecule. They compared the chemical make-up of the hemoglobin from a sickle cell with that of a normal red cell. First, by means of enzymes, they cut the long coils of sickle cell hemoglobin into twenty-six smaller pieces. They then placed a drop of solution containing these fragments on a moist piece of filter paper and passed an electric current through it. The pieces moved away from one another and spread out in a line across the paper. This sheet of paper was placed in another solution so that the edge with the spread-out pieces was moistened. The solution crept up the paper carrying the fragments with it.

The hemoglobin pieces ascended the paper, but at different rates, and came to rest at various levels. By spraying the paper with a dye, the spots became visible and a pattern of smear spots resembling fingerprints appeared.

Each kind of protein has a different "fingerprint" by

which it can be recognized and identified. Hemoglobin from a normal cell was now "fingerprinted" and compared with that of sickle hemoglobin. The fingerprints were the same, spot for spot, except in one place. The two mismatched spots were then analyzed and each was found to contain eight amino acids, seven of which were the same. Again, there was just one difference: the sixth amino acid in normal hemoglobin was glutamic acid and the sixth place in the sickle chain contained valine.

Normal   val-his-leu-thr-pro-GLUTAMIC ACID-glu-lys
Sickle   val-his-leu-thr-pro-VALINE-   glu-lys

There is just one difference in one amino acid in a chain of three hundred and this makes the difference between health and disease, between life and death. Incredible as this may seem, just one wrong amino acid link in the protein chain of life and it collapses. Here is evidence that the order of the bases in a particular gene determines the order of the amino acids in a protein molecule. The Crick-Watson model of DNA and the concept that the order of the bases fixes the sequence of the amino acids in a protein, explain the difference. By changing a single base in the DNA chain, one amino acid is altered and an abnormal protein is produced, the hemoglobin of sickle-cell anemia.

Missing Molecules

Many of the chemical reactions in your body take place step by step in assembly-line fashion. For example, the

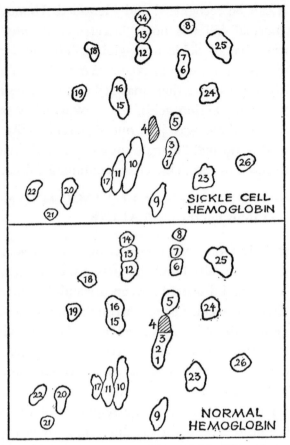

Fingerprints of normal and sickle cell hemoglobin differ only on one spot

color of your skin, hair, and eyes is due to a brownish-black coloring material called melanin (MEL-a-nin). Dark-skinned people manufacture an abundance of this pigment; those with blond hair, blue eyes, and a very light complexion make much less. However, all people make some melanin. This pigment is produced from the amino acid called tyrosine (TIE-row-sean), which is made from still another amino acid, phenylalanine. There are at least two chemical steps in producing melanin. Phenylalanine is changed to tyrosine, and tyrosine is converted to melanin, and at least two enzymes are needed, one for each step. If either enzyme is missing, the chemical production line is halted and melanin is not produced. Occasionally children are born with white hair, very fair skin, and pink eyes. They are referred to as albinos (al-BUY-noze). Their bodies lack the ability to make the enzyme necessary for converting tyrosine to melanin. Hence they lack coloring material in their hair and skin, and eyes (the eyes are pink because there is no pigment in them and what you see is the color of the blood in the back of the eye). Albinism is a hereditary condition resulting from the mutation of a single gene. Albino children may come from parents with black, brown, or normal white skins. This hereditary condition, as the result of a mutation, is a striking example of how the loss of a single enzyme among thousands can produce startling results.

Inborn Error in Metabolism—PKU

The mutation of a single gene is also responsible for one type of feeblemindedness caused by the inability of the body to metabolize the amino acid phenylalanine. Because the enzyme which normally oxidizes phenylalanine is missing at birth, this amino acid accumulates in the body, and is excreted in the urine. This condition is known as phenylketonuria (fen-il-kee-tow-NOR-ee-uh), or PKU. The mutation deprives the organism of its ability to synthesize the missing enzyme without which the body chemistry is seriously disturbed, leading to brain damage.

Fortunately, PKU can be detected in infants a few weeks after birth and before phenylalanine affects the brain. By feeding PKU infants a diet low in phenylalanine, all the physical and mental symptoms are suppressed. The "inborn error in metabolism" can be corrected and these children can live normal lives.

Mad Molecules—Cancer

DNA is now suspected of having some relation to the cause of cancer. This is a disease in which some of the cells in an organism suddenly go berserk and begin a career of uncontrolled reproduction. Normally, cells are law abiding members of the body community, subject to the rules and regulations set down by the organism. Each cell has its place and its responsibility written down in its DNA code. Skin cells have a definite size, shape, function, and rate of reproduction. New skin cells are produced only where and when they are needed by the organism. However, a skin cell may suddenly embark on a reproduction rampage in utter disregard for the other skin cells around it. It may produce cells completely unlike its neighbors. These cells are outlaws. They create other cells which follow in their footsteps. Within a short time, a whole mass of wildly dividing cells may pile up on the skin to form a lump of cancerous tissue, a tumor. One or more of these rabid reproducers at the bottom of the cancerous tumor may break away, anchor itself elsewhere in the body and continue its cancerous career of corrupting and disrupting the living organism. The unlimited capacity of cancer cells to reproduce eventually leads to the death of the host.

Cancer-Inducing DNA

What makes a normal cell turn into a raving reproducing cancer cell? There are so many suspects that you can list them alphabetically, starting with "A" for atomic fallout, "B" for bruises, "C" for cigarettes, and so forth down to the end of the alphabet. Regardless of who the guilty party or parties are, cancer is triggered by a change in the genetic instructions of a cell. A cancer cell is distinctly different from a normal cell in structure and function. In addition, cancer cells breed more cancer cells like themselves. The altered genetic code which spells out cancer is duplicated and passed on to all the daughter cells.

Cancer has been induced, experimentally, in plants and animals by a whole host of influences among which X rays and chemicals are the best known. Many of these cancer-causing agents change the genes and chromosomes of the cell. Heavy doses of X rays, for example, cripple the chromosomes and in some instances create cancer cells. From time to time, the idea is advanced that cancer is an infectious disease caused by viruses. The popularity of this virus theory waxes and wanes like phases of the moon. In 1911 Peyton Rous of the Rockefeller Institute proved that a virus caused cancer in chickens. Since then, other viruses have been discovered which produce cancer in rats, mice, frogs, deer, rabbits, hamsters, monkeys, cats, dogs, horses, and cows—in practically all animals except man.

In 1962 at the National Cancer Institute, Dr. Sarah Steward and Dr. Bernice Eddy found a virus capable of producing many kinds of cancerous tumors in rats, mice, and hamsters. Because of its ability to induce so many different kinds of tumors, this virus was named polyoma. When this virus was stripped of its protein coat and its naked DNA injected into laboratory animals, tumors appeared in some of the animals. Polyoma DNA was the first molecule found capable of both causing a virus infection and inducing cancer.

Viruses and Cancer

How do viruses cause cancer? We do not know but we can make some educated guesses based on what we know about viruses, genes, and the cell. Both viruses and genes are bits of nucleoproteins with the genetic instructions contained in the nucleic acid. A virus injects only its nucleic acid into a cell and once its DNA (or RNA in the case of TMV) is inside the cell any one of several events may occur. The viral DNA may take over and use the cell to make hundreds of other viruses like itself, in which case the cell is destroyed. Or the viruses may cause one of several diseases: common cold, influenza, chicken pox, measles, or poliomyelitis. A virus may attach itself to the bacterial DNA and "pretend" to be part of the genetic apparatus of its host. Viral DNA can live in peace and harmony within the bacterium for many generations without making its presence felt or known. However, exposing such virus-carrying cells to X rays or chemicals sometimes "awakens" these concealed particles and they suddenly begin to reproduce and destroy the cell. Finally a virus may make a cell lose its control and plunge it into a wild orgy of reproduction forming strange and abnormal cancer cells. Possibly this is how viruses in all animals including man launch a cell on a cancerous career.

At present there is no clear-cut answer to the question of whether viruses cause cancer in humans. In the past few years, over 200 new viruses have been discovered in humans and in many instances the diseases caused by them are unknown. Basically, the life processes in man are very similar to those in other animals and it seems reasonable to assume that viruses may be responsible for some kinds of cancer in humans.

Recently, Dr. Robert Huebner of the National Institute of Health reported that he inoculated hamsters with human viruses, many of which cause respiratory illnesses much like the common cold and in a few months these animals developed tumors. One of the greatest difficulties in isolating human cancer viruses is that once they enter a cell these viruses seem to "disappear." They shed their protein coats and probably become just another strand of nucleic acid in the cell.

A giant step forward in the study of viruses as agents of human cancer is the development of tissue culture techniques, that is, growing human cells in test tubes. Cells from the amniotic membrane covering the baby at birth and other cells have been grown in tissue culture and infected with viruses. With this new tool, efforts are being made to hunt down possible cancer-causing viruses of humans.

11

DNA—The Molecule of the Future

Recent years have been among the busiest and most fruitful in the history of biology, due primarily to the tremendous progress in unraveling the structure and the function of DNA and RNA. These nucleic acids are revolutionizing our thinking about the nature of life and the mechanisms that control it. The crucial breakthrough in probing DNA's secret code of life appears to be imminent. Scientists are confident that it is only a matter of time before they will be able to read the entire genetic code in the genes and chromosomes. Once this barrier has been cleared, man should be able to "write" his own genetic messages or change the message according to his specifications. It is not beyond the realm of possibility that in the future man will be able to engineer and plan an organism just as he does a machine. Molecular biological engineering may be one of the important professions of the scientist of tomorrow. Let us look into the scientific crystal ball and try to predict what DNA will be doing in the immediate future.

Life from a Test Tube

Scientific talk about creating life in a test tube from dead chemicals is not idle chatter. This project is no longer in the realm of science fiction. It is being pursued seriously by some of the outstanding scientists. Now that cell-free systems for making proteins have been mastered, the technique is being applied to breeding DNA in a test tube. How successful we have been may be judged from an announcement made in August 1962 by two independent groups of scientists who reported the birth of live viruses from dead chemicals. Dr. Samuel C. Wildman and Young Tai Kim of the University of California, and Dr. George W. Cochran of the Utah State University prepared extracts of RNA from the tobacco mosaic virus, TMV, which they placed in a cell-free system with the six submolecular parts of RNA. The RNA threads, serving as a template, assembled the six dead submolecules into a living TMV virus. These test tube viruses, which were being created at the rate of more than 3 billion per minute, were no different from those normally made inside the cells of the tobacco plant.

Equally sensational is the creation of "living" DNA molecules by two scientists in 1964. Dr. Kornberg, you will remember, made DNA that was chemically and phys-

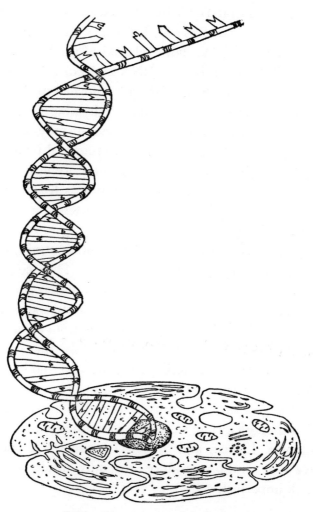

DNA—The molecule of the future

ically like natural DNA but it was not alive and could not reproduce. Dr. Rose M. Litman of the University of Colorado and Dr. Waclaw Szybalski of the University of Wisconsin have synthesized DNA molecules that do have the ability to reproduce. They put a normal strain of bacteria on a diet containing labeled thymine (T), one of the four bases present in DNA. These microbes produced tagged DNA molecules which were removed from them. The tagged bacteria DNA molecules were used as a primer for making test tube DNA just as Kornberg had done. Now came the critical step—to test the synthetic DNA for "life."

The synthetic DNA was fed to another strain of bacteria which were genetically defective. They could not make certain chemicals, including two amino acids. Unless these "sick" bacteria were fed these substances, they starved to death. Since the primer came from normal bacteria capable of making these foodstuffs, the synthetic DNA contained the genetic information for making them.

When the artificial DNA was fed to the defective bacteria, the genetic defect was corrected. The bacteria, as well as their offspring, were able to synthesize the missing substances. Litman and Szybalski made DNA that was "alive"—it could reproduce but only inside a living, though imperfect, cell.

Reading Genes and Chromosomes

Current research in molecular biology is bringing us closer to the exact DNA structure of the gene. The genetic dictionary that Ochoa, Nirenberg, and Matthaei are writing is based on relatively simple synthetic RNA molecules. They are learning the A-B-C of the amino acid alphabet from the proteins assembled by the coded molecules which they make. The problem is to isolate a gene and read its genetic message. No one has as yet determined the base sequence in a gene, although Dr. Seymour Benzer of Purdue University has made serious efforts to split the gene and to make detailed maps of its inner structure. With the help of chemically induced mutations, Benzer has located the position of about 400 places, each representing a pair of bases, in two sections of the DNA molecule in the bacteriophage T4. He hopes to find chemicals that will change specific bases in the chain and so ultimately determine the number and the sequence of the bases in the gene.

By 1962 Dr. Robert S. Edgar of the California Institute of Technology, who also utilized chemically induced mutations, had pinned down about fifty of the hundred genes in the T4 bacteriophage. He discovered the function of the proteins produced by these genes. For example, four of these genes produce the enzymes which assemble the tadpole-like head of the phage.

And in 1964, a scientist reported that she picked out a gene from one kind of cell and put it into another cell, giving that cell a new trait. Dr. Muriel Rogers of the Rockefeller Institute isolated the DNA molecule from a single bacterial chromosome and broke it into small fragments, each containing a single gene. She was working with genes which enable bacteria to resist the effects of certain drugs. When one of these genes for drug resistance was introduced into bacterial cells not resistant to these drugs, they acquired the ability to withstand the drugs.

RNA—The Memory Molecule

A most surprising facet of nucleic acid research is seen in experiments suggesting that RNA plays an important part in memory. Dr. Holger Hyden, of the University of Goteberg in Sweden, found that nerve cells are very rich in RNA and that the amount of this nucleic acid varies with age and mental activities. Holger believes that memory is stored in the RNA molecules of the nerve cells. He thinks that the four bases of RNA can be rearranged to encode and store every bit of information that the brain receives like a giant computer.

Some of the experiments testing the theory that RNA is the memory molecule were conducted with simple flatworms called planarians. When these worms are cut in half, they regenerate into two new planarians. Robert Thompson and James V. McConnell at the University of Texas taught planarians to turn their heads when a strong light was shone on them. Later another group at the University of Michigan cut trained planarians in two and the halves were permitted to grow back missing parts. They found that both the worms that grew from the tail pieces as well as those from the head pieces "remembered" what they had been taught.

To find out if memory is stored in RNA molecules, William C. Corning, working at the University of Roch-

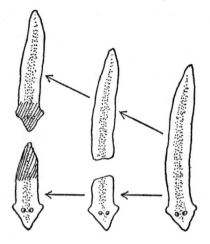

Planarians cut in half grow
back missing parts

ester, repeated the experiment performed by the Michigan group, except that the pieces of the trained worms were permitted to grow back the missing parts in a solution containing an enzyme that destroys RNA. Corning found the worms that grew new heads from old tail pieces remembered nothing but those that kept their heads and acquired new tails did remember. The RNA-destroying enzyme erased the memory in the tails but not in the heads of these worms.

Another group at the University of Michigan carried this experiment one step further and obtained unbelievable results. After teaching a group of worms to turn their heads, they were chopped up and fed to an untrained group of worms. As a control, another batch of untutored worms was fed to untutored worms. The worms on a diet of educated worms remembered their lessons, but those on a diet of uneducated worms did not.

Correcting DNA Deficiencies and Disorders

DNA is also seen as the hope for treating and possibly curing many human ailments, particularly those resulting from defects in the genes. You will recall that sickle-cell anemia is caused by a single mistake in the single amino acid in the protein hemoglobin and that feeble-mindedness in PKU is the result of a missing enzyme. In both cases, DNA seems to be at fault.

When man has finally become scientifically literate enough to read DNA messages, it should be possible to pinpoint the errors and correct them. It is conceivable that such mistakes in the DNA chain can be rectified by chemicals or by supplying the sufferers with normal DNA which produces the proper proteins to correct the damage. Recent experiments indicate that missing enzymes can be replaced by DNA. At the University of Wisconsin, human cells lacking the ability to make a particular enzyme were grown in test tubes outside the body. By feeding these defective cells DNA extracts from normal cells, they were able not only to regain the ability to manufacture the missing enzyme and function normally, but the DNA donated trait was inherited.

Evidence is piling up linking viruses and human cancer. Circumstantial scientific evidence points to the virus as one of the criminals which alter the genetic coding of the cell and initiate cancer. Viruses are being discovered in persons suffering from certain kinds of cancer such as blood cancer, leukemia (lew-KEY-me-uh). There is however no proof that these viruses cause the disease; they may be innocent bystanders. Many of these viruses are very similar in appearance to viruses that cause leukemia in mice. Moreover, in 1963, Dr. Maurice Green at the St. Louis University Medical School found a striking similarity between DNA molecules of two human viruses that produce cancer in baby hamsters and that of polyoma, the powerful cancer-producing virus in animals. The DNA of these three cancer-causing viruses is more like that in normal human cells than is the DNA of a non-cancer-producing virus. Dr. Green speculates that since the DNA in these cancer-causing viruses are so much like that in normal human cells, they can replace or change the normal DNA and transform a normal cell into a cancerous cell. The progress being made in cancer research is so rapid many scientists feel confident that a breakthrough in the human cancer-virus link is very close.

The Age of DNA

It is becoming increasingly apparent that DNA has opened new vistas in science and has stirred the imagination of scientists. DNA is extending our knowledge and understanding of the nature of life on the molecular level. It is giving us new insights into the workings of the mind and the body. Hope of the conquest of hereditary and viruses disease as well as cancer grows stronger as DNA research expands. The creation of new forms of life also looms large. And finally the mastery of DNA may mean the mastery of man and his destiny. As we climb the ladder of life, DNA points to the limitless possibilities for research to improve the lot of man on earth.

For Further Reading

Asimov, Isaac, *The Genetic Code,* The New American Library, New York, 1963

Fraenkel-Conrat, H., *Design and Function at the Threshold of Life: The Viruses,* Academic Press, New York, 1962

Gerard, Ralph, *Unresting Cells,* Harper and Row, New York, 1961

Hutchins, Carleen M., *Life's Key—DNA,* Coward-McCann, Inc., New York, 1961

Moore, Ruth, *The Coil of Life,* Alfred A. Knopf, New York, 1961

Morowitz, Harold J., *Life and The Physical Sciences,* Holt, Rinehart & Winston, New York, 1963

Stanley, W. M. and Valens, E. G., *Viruses and the Nature of Life,* E. P. Dutton, New York, 1961

Weidel, Wolfhard, *Virus,* University of Michigan Press, Ann Arbor, Mich., 1959

Williams, Greer, *Virus Hunters,* Alfred A. Knopf, New York, 1959

Index

* Page numbers in italics refer to illustrations.

About the Author and Artist

EDWARD FRANKEL received a B.S. degree in biology at the College of the City of New York, an M.A. in Science Education at Columbia University, and a Ph.D. at Yeshiva University. A teacher at the Bronx High School of Science for many years, he numbers among his former students many leading scientists. Dr. Frankel is Associate Professor of Education at Hunter College, as well as chairman of the Science Department of Yeshiva University High School and science coordinator of the Yeshiva University high schools. He writes widely for publications in the educational fields and is also well known as a lecturer.

ANNE MARIE JAUSS, illustrator of fifty books, has written and illustrated several books of her own on nature subjects. She studied art in Munich, Germany, her birthplace. For fourteen years she lived in Lisbon, Portugal, working as a painter, designer, and illustrator. Miss Jauss came to the United States in 1946 and makes her home in rural New Jersey.